PRENTICE-HALL

FOUNDATIONS OF **DEVELOPMENTAL BIOLOGY** SERIES

PRENTICE-HALL

FOUNDATIONS OF **DEVELOPMENTAL BIOLOGY** SERIES

Clement L. Markert, Editor

FERTILIZATION   *C. R. Austin*

PLANT DEVELOPMENT   *Arthur W. Galston*

DIFFERENTIATION   *H. E. Lehman*

DEVELOPMENTAL GENETICS*   *Clement L. Markert*

BIOCHEMICAL AND PHYSIOLOGICAL
DIFFERENTIATION   *David Prescott*

CELL AND TISSUE INTERACTIONS   *J. P. Trinkaus*

* Published jointly in Prentice-Hall's *Foundations of Modern Genetics Series*

FERTILIZATION

C. R. Austin

Delta Regional Primate Research Center
Tulane University

PRENTICE-HALL, INC.   Englewood Cliffs, New Jersey

FOUNDATIONS OF DEVELOPMENTAL BIOLOGY SERIES

Fertilization
C-31441-P
C-31443-C

PRENTICE-HALL INTERNATIONAL, INC., *London*
PRENTICE-HALL OF AUSTRALIA, PTY., LTD., *Sydney*
PRENTICE-HALL OF CANADA, LTD., *Toronto*
PRENTICE-HALL OF INDIA (PRIVATE) LTD., *New Delhi*
PRENTICE-HALL OF JAPAN, INC., *Tokyo*

Foundations of DEVELOPMENTAL BIOLOGY

The development of organisms is so wondrous and yet so common that it has compelled man's attention and aroused his curiosity from earliest times. But developmental processes have proved to be complex and difficult to understand, and little progress was made for hundreds of years. By the beginning of this century, increasingly skillful experimentation began to accelerate the slow advance in our understanding of development. Most important in recent years has been the rapid progress in the related disciplines of biochemistry and genetics—progress that has now made possible an experimental attack on developmental problems at the molecular level. Many old and intractable problems are taking on a fresh appeal, and a tense expectancy pervades the biological community. Exciting advances are surely imminent.

New insights into the structure and function of cells are moving the principal problems of developmental biology into the center of scientific attention, and increasing numbers of biologists are focusing their research efforts on these problems. Moreover, new tools and experimental designs are now available to help in their solution.

At this critical stage of scientific development a fresh assessment is needed. This series of books in developmental biology is designed to provide essential background material and then to examine the frontier where exciting advances are occurring or expected. Each book is written by a leading investigator actively concerned with the problems and concepts he discusses. Students at intermediate and advanced levels of preparation should find these books informative, stimulating, and useful. Collectively, they present an authoritative and penetrating analysis of the major problems and concepts of developmental biology, together with a critical appraisal of the experimental tools and designs that make developmental biology so exciting and challenging today.

CLEMENT L. MARKERT

Preface

This book is intended primarily for the use of students and research workers who seek a general knowledge of fertilization in its comparative aspects, and of the various cytological, physiological, and behavioral mechanisms concerned with the union of the gametes. My aim has been to present information on an extensive range of animal and vegetable forms, on representatives at least of all major groups, while purposely limiting the space given to organisms that have been popular research materials. I have tried not to obscure the contributions made by the less commonly investigated species in order the better to highlight underlying generalizations and principles.

The first chapter contains a brief account of the structure and function of the cell, and the salient features of mitosis, meiosis, and cell division. This was included partly as an introduction to the gametes as highly specialized cells, and partly to take the burden of general description from later chapters wherein the special properties of gametes are set forth. It is followed by a discussion of the significance of fertilization in the animal economy, in which I have attempted to explain clearly the respective roles of mitosis, meiosis, and syngamy in the propagation and development of the race.

Instead of providing the usual list of references to publications at the end of the book, I have set out a classified and partly annotated Selected Bibliography, in the belief that this will prove of greater value, especially to readers unfamiliar with the field and to those who require texts giving comprehensive treatment of selected topics.

It is a pleasure to express my gratitude to the following for permission to reproduce photographs and for kindly providing excellent prints for this purpose: Dr. D. G. Szollosi (Fig. 1.2); Dr. T. Nagano and the Japan Electron Optics Co. (Fig. 1.5); Dr. R. A. Kille and *Experimental Cell Research* (Fig. 6.2); and Dr. E. B. Simmel, Dr. D. A. Karnofsky, and the Rockefeller Institute Press (Fig. 6.3). Fig. 6.8a and b was reproduced by permission from *Experimental Cell Research*, and Fig. 7.4 by permission from the *Journal of Cellular and Comparative Physiology*.

The book was written while I was a member of the External Scientific Staff of the Medical Research Council (G.B.), and in its preparation I depended heavily upon the library facilities at the Marine Biological Laboratory, Woods Hole, Massachusetts, and at the Departments of Zoology and Botany of the University of Cambridge, England. My sincere thanks go to Dr. Albert Tyler for critically reviewing the text and offering many helpful comments and suggestions, to Mrs. Heather Clough for invaluable service in the initial preparation of photographs and drawings, and to my wife for unstinted care and effort spent in typing the manuscript.

C. R. AUSTIN

Covington, Louisiana
July, 1965

Contents

FERTILIZATION

ONE

General Cytology

The cell consists of nucleus and cytoplasm. The "resting" or interphase nucleus is filled with nuclear sap or nucleoplasm, in which are suspended one or more nucleoli and the chromosomes; it is bounded by the nuclear membrane. The cytoplasm is made up of a ground substance, the cell sap or hyaloplasm, in which are distributed the cell organelles and a variety of inclusions. The chief organelles are the mitochondria, plastids, Golgi apparatus, and the division center. The inclusions take the form of droplets, granules, crystalloids, and vesicles, representing stored food materials, secretions such as hormones and proenzymes, pigments, and waste products. The cytoplasm is limited by the plasma membrane, beyond which extends the extraneous coat. Plant and bacterial cells are surrounded in addition by a cell wall. Between cells composing animal tissues there normally exist stable regions of cell contact, where close approximation is achieved.

Nucleus

Nucleoplasm

Most of the space within the nucleus is occupied by the nucleoplasm, which may be gel-like but generally has a fluid consistency. It appears homogeneous by electron microscopy. Its main chemical components are proteins and a little ribonucleic acid (RNA).

Nucleoli

One or more nucleoli occur in nuclei, but the number is apt to vary, for nucleoli can usually coalesce. Sometimes they are spherical,

1

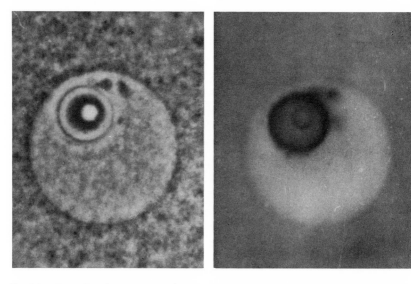

Fig. 1.1.   The nucleus (germinal vesicle) of the rat primary oöcyte as photographed by phase-contrast (left) and ultraviolet (right) microscopy. Intensity of ultraviolet absorption is related to concentration of nucleic acids, the dense band around the nucleolus representing the nucleolus-associated chromatin.

refractile bodies of homogeneous ultrastructure (Figs. 1.1, 1.2, and 5.20); in other cells, they are irregular in form, and electron microscopy shows them to consist of an amorphous part and a filamentous part, the latter being termed the nucleoloneme. Generally, nucleoli are invested with an irregular mass of material, the nucleolus-associated chromatin, which is rich in deoxyribonucleic acid (DNA) (Figs. 1.1 and 1.4). The nucleoli of tissue cells, especially of those that are in active protein synthesis, normally contain RNA. Nucleoli are formed at specific points in certain chromosomes, the nucleolus organizers, of which there is as a rule only one for each chromosome set.[1] Just before mitosis, the nucleoli fade and disappear as the chromosomes condense; they reappear after mitosis as the chromosomes resume the extended state.

Chromosomes

The chromosomes are distinctive for their high content of DNA; their importance lies in the fact that they carry the main determinants of hereditary characters, the genes. In the interphase nucleus they exist in a highly extended state and usually cannot be seen; they

---

[1] Exceptions include amphibian oöcyte nuclei, in which occur hundreds of small bodies termed nucleoli, and many metazoan pronuclei—as in Fig. 5.20.

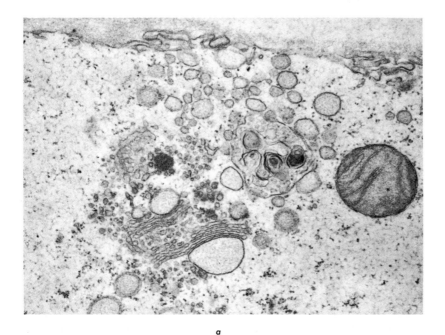

a

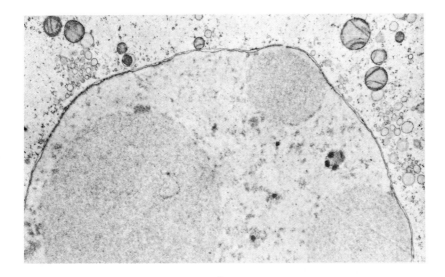

b

Fig. 1.2. Electron micrographs of rat eggs, showing: (a) Parallel arrays of cytomembranes and vesicles of the Golgi apparatus, and a mitochondrion with the form of cristae commonly found in mammalian eggs. Magnification: 25,000 ×. (b) Portion of a pronucleus; note the double nuclear membrane, with pores at irregular intervals, and the circumscribed regions of higher electron density representing the nucleoli. Two or three mitochondria are visible to left and right above the pronucleus. Magnification: 10,000 ×. Photographs by courtesy of D. G. Szollosi.

assume their familiar rodlike form during cell division, when the nuclear membrane and nucleoli disappear and the nucleus is represented by a group of condensed chromosomes. The over-all shape of a chromosome, whether it appears as an I, as an L, or as a V, depends on the position of the centromere, which may be located terminally (in acrocentric chromosomes), subterminally (in submetacentric chromosomes), or medially (in metacentric chromosomes). The centromere is a small DNA-free constriction that is seemingly the point of insertion of the spindle fiber; the behavior of chromosomes in mitosis and meiosis suggests that traction is applied to the chromosome at the centromere.

Genes are discrete regions of chromosomes in which the actual hereditary determinants reside. The current view is that the molecular structure of DNA is in the form of a double helix consisting of two polynucleotide chains linked by pairs of purine and pyrimidine bases. It is believed that the genetic information is coded in the order in which these bases are disposed.

In many lower vertebrates, the chromosomes in the oöcyte nucleus (the germinal vesicle) display a distinctive form that gives them the name *lampbrush* or *lateral-loop chromosomes*. As such, each consists of a much extended pair of threadlike chromatids (half chromosomes), which are linked to each other at intervals but elsewhere are thrown into a large number of lateral loops. Chromosomes in this state are thought to have a special synthetic activity associated with oöcyte development.

The number of chromosomes in the somatic nuclei of an animal is usually characteristic, both for various tissues of the individual and for individuals of the species. The mature germ cells, however, have half the corresponding somatic number[2]; the complement of chromosomes in these cells is known as the haploid number (or n). The somatic number is referred to as the diploid number (or $2n$), for it is made up of two complete haploid sets of chromosomes. Reduction from the diploid to the haploid occurs in meiosis, which, in brown algae and most animals, is a feature of gametogenesis. In some tissues (liver, neoplasms), the nuclei contain more than two haploid sets and so display the condition of polyploidy, of which various levels exist— triploidy ($3n$), tetraploidy ($4n$), and so forth. In some animals, e.g., the honeybee, the individuals do not all have the same chromosome number, the females being diploid and the males haploid. Errors of germ-cell maturation or of fertilization can also give rise to variations

---

[2] This is a general statement that holds true particularly for the higher animals, but there are many exceptions in other organisms, notably the insects, in which complications such as "limited chromosomes," "chromosome elimination," and multiple sex chromosomes disturb the somatic: germ-cell chromosome ratios.

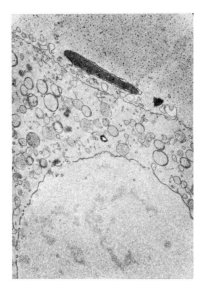
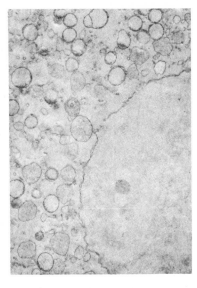

a   b

Fig. 1.3. Electron micrographs of rabbit eggs, showing pronuclei with double membranes and pores. Mitochondria are visible as rounded bodies with few cristae and these arranged circumferentially to give the bodies the appearance of having incomplete double walls. In (a) a tangential section of the head of a supplementary spermatozoon can be seen lying just above the plasma membrane. Magnification: (a) 2,200 ×, (b) 3,300 ×.

in ploidy, leading not only to the production of individuals with different numbers of haploid sets but also to the production of those with irregular numbers of chromosomes. The irregularities may diverge but little from normal (aneuploidy)—as with trisomy ($2n + 1$), where one chromosome is represented three times instead of the normal twice (e.g., trisomy-21, which leads to Mongolism in man), or when a single deletion gives monosomy ($2n - 1$), where one chromosome is unmatched (e.g., monosomy-X, which leads to Turner's syndrome in man). On the other hand, the divergence may be so large that the chromosome number is not clearly related to any multiple of the haploid (heteroploidy).

In a number of animals, each haploid set contains one chromosome that is a sex chromosome (designated X, Y, W, or Z), the rest being distinguished as autosomes. In mammals, the X chromosome is female-determining and the Y strongly male-determining; female animals have in each set XX and males XY ("male heterogamety"). In the Lepidoptera and Trichoptera, and in birds, ZZ is the chromosome constitution of males and WZ that of females ("female heterogamety").[3] Among

---

[3] Sometimes the Y (or the W) is missing, as seems to be true for the vole *Microtus montebelli* (♂ = XO) and the fowl *Gallus domesticus* (♀ = OZ).

the fishes, some species display the X-Y system and others the W-Z system.

Nuclear membrane

The membrane bounding the interphase nucleus cannot be directly perceived by light microscopy, since it is less than 0.1 μ thick, but its presence can be demonstrated with the aid of microdissecting needles. It is possible, too, to disrupt the cytoplasm of a cell by chemical means and liberate the nucleus, the integrity of which then depends upon the presence of an intact nuclear membrane. By electron microscopy, the nuclear membrane is found to consist of two layers, each about 100 Å thick and separated by a space of a little more than that (Figs. 1.2 and 1.3). The continuity of the nuclear membrane is interrupted by a large number of holes or pores around which the inner and outer layers are joined. The pores, which have a diameter of 400 to 700 Å, apparently permit actual confluence between nucleoplasm and cytoplasm and would be large enough to allow even protein molecules free passage, but there is evidence that a fine diaphragm extending across each pore limits transfer of materials between nucleus and cytoplasm. The outer layer of the nuclear membrane is continuous also at several points with the endoplasmic reticulum of the cytoplasm.

Cytoplasm

Hyaloplasm

The ground substance of the cytoplasm in which the organelles and inclusions are suspended accounts for the bulk of the cytoplasm but appears structureless by light microscopy. Electron microscopy, on the other hand, reveals a wealth of detail in the hyaloplasm, which is seen to contain numerous minute (100 to 150 Å) particles—the ribosomes—and membranous structures of varying arrangement and complexity—the cytomembranes or endoplasmic reticulum. The ribosomes consist largely of RNA and protein and are responsible for the basophilia of the cytoplasm. When the cytomembranes are numerous and arranged in rows of flattened cysternae lined on one side with attached ribosomes (as is often the case), the complex is referred to as ergastoplasm. Such a system is best seen in actively secreting cells such as those of the pancreatic acinae. In other cells, particularly rapidly growing ones such as oöcytes, cytomembranes are scarce and fragmentary, and the large majority of the ribosomes lie free.

Mitochondria

Mitochondria have long been observed by light microscopy; they can take different forms, such as granules, rods, and threads,

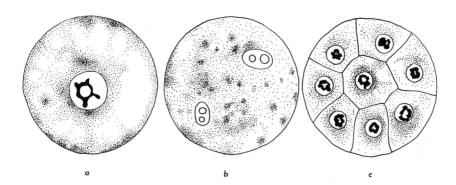

Fig. 1.4. Differential fluorescence induced in living rat eggs by treatment with acridine orange and ultraviolet irradiation (solid black = DNA; stipple = mononucleotides). In the primary oöcyte (a) and the 8-cell egg (c), the nucleolus-associated chromatin is well developed; it is not detectable in the pronuclei (b), partly because they are haploid and partly because the pronuclear DNA is apparently distributed through the nucleoplasm. Most of the fluorescent cytoplasmic particles were probably mitochondria.

that are readily interconvertible, and they can be stained, even in living cells, with Janus green B. The distribution of mitochondria varies with the type of cellular activity: in dividing cells, the mitochondria tend to gather about the equator of the spindle, while in early oöcytes they abound near the Golgi apparatus, and in cleaving eggs they closely invest the nucleus (Fig. 1.4). In ultrastructure, the mitochondrion is seen to be limited by two membranes, 60 to 80 Å apart, each of which is a double structure, having 20-Å layers separated by a space of similar dimension. The inner membrane is thrown up into a number of tall septa; these partially subdivide the cavity within the mitochondrion, which is occupied by a dense, more or less homogeneous matrix (Figs. 1.2 and 1.3). It has been suggested that the outer membrane is continuous at one or two points with the cytomembranes and hence eventually with the nuclear and plasma membranes. Mitochondria are intimately connected with the energy metabolism of the cell and contain a complex system of enzymes, including those of the Krebs' cycle.

Plastids

The characteristic color of green plant cells is attributable to the presence of chlorophyll, which is disposed in numerous bodies, the chloroplasts. These represent one form of plastid, of which two other forms also occur: chromoplasts, which contain pigments other than chlorophyll, such as the carotenes and xanthophylls; and leucoplasts, which carry stored materials such as starch, oil, and protein. The plastid is a saclike structure, limited by a double membrane and enclosing dense arrays of fine parallel lamellae. Plastids have a curiously independent existence: it seems that they cannot be generated *de novo* in plant cells but must be derived by the division of pre-existing plastids. They are transmitted from parent plant to progeny in the seed as proplastids, a diminutive, pigment-free form, and except for the leuco-plasts, which remain colorless, they acquire pigment later.

Golgi apparatus

The Golgi structure takes so many and varied forms that some investigators deny its existence as a single entity. It can appear as a dense reticular mass of argentophilic or osmiophilic bodies, enclosing argentophobic or osmiophobic inclusions, disposed beside the nucleus and often around the centrosome, as in early oöcytes and spermatocytes. Or it may be found as a number of small bodies scattered throughout the cytoplasm, as in the mammalian oötid. By electron microscopy, it is identified as a system of cytomembranes lined on one surface with ribosomes and gathered into a number of parallel cysternae, together with a surrounding array of vesicles and vacuoles (Fig. 1.2). The vacuoles sometimes contain dense, homogeneous granules of presumably secretory material, as is the case with the zymogen granules in pancreatic cells. This and other observations suggest that the Golgi apparatus is often concerned with the process of secretion.

Division center

In most cells, two small bodies, the centrioles, lie beside the interphase nucleus within a circumscribed region of clear cytoplasm referred to as the centrosome. As the time for mitosis and cell division approaches, the centrioles separate and move to opposite poles of the nucleus. A spindle forms between them, and the chromosomes become arranged at its equator. Replication of centrioles, whereby each centriole gives rise to a daughter centriole, begins when the mother centrioles separate, so that when the interphase nuclei are reformed there once again lies beside each nucleus a centrosome containing two centrioles.

In ultrastructure, the centriole commonly takes the form of a short cylinder, the wall of which contains nine triplet fibers running the length of the cylinder. Daughter centrioles are generated from the side of the mother centrioles, projecting at right angles to the long axis; this angular relationship persists throughout interphase and is thought to determine the orientation of the next spindle relative to the previous one (Fig. 1.5).

Centrioles have in addition two quite different functions. They play a role in the formation of cilia and flagella, which seem to develop as direct continuations of single centrioles; cilia and flagella display for

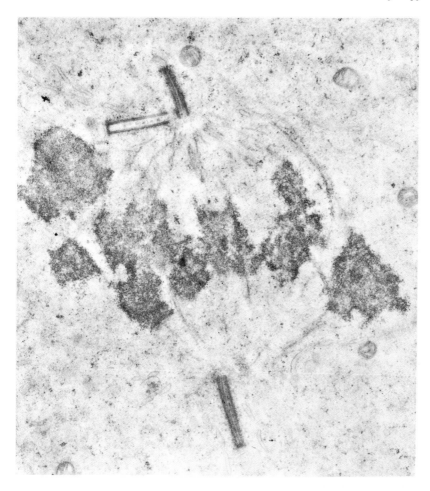

Fig. 1.5. Electron micrograph of a rooster spermatocyte with unusually well displayed centrioles at the spindle poles. From *The World Through the Electron Microscope: Biology,* N. Higashi, compiler (Japan Electron Optics Co., Ltd., 1961). Photograph by courtesy of T. Nagano.

the most part a ring of nine double fibers with a pair of fibers passing up the center. They also give rise in much the same way to the distal regions of retinal rods and cones.

Plasma membrane

The cytoplasm is limited externally by a plasma membrane, the physical and chemical properties of which regulate exchanges between cell and environment. It is generally believed that the membrane consists of a bimolecular layer of lipoid molecules, of which the nonpolar groups are directed toward each other and the polar groups outward. On both surfaces, protein molecules are disposed with their nonpolar groups directed into the lipoid layer and their polar groups outward. Electron microscopy affords good support for the bimolecular theory, since by this means it is demonstrable that the plasma membrane consists of two osmiophilic layers each about 25 Å thick, separated by a layer of low electron density of about the same thickness—dimensions that fit the molecular model reasonably well. Such a membrane is often called a unit membrane and in the form just described it seems to occur in the majority of cells. Some cells, however, have more robust plasma membranes. Thus, cells of the rabbit intestinal epithelium have been shown to have a plasma membrane consisting of two layers 40 Å thick, with an intermediate layer of 25 Å, giving a total thickness of 105 Å. The mature sea-urchin oöcyte appears to have a still thicker membrane before sperm entry (see "Eggs of sea urchin and rabbit" in Chapter 3). The membrane of the human erythrocyte is evidently compound, with a thickness of 200–300 Å.

The cell surface is rarely smooth and uncomplicated, almost always showing a few to many small, fingerlike projections known as microvilli, and invaginations of varying depth; both forms are lined with plasma membrane (Figs. 1.2 and 1.3). The microvilli of most somatic cells are of the order of 0.6 to 0.8 μ long and 0.1 μ in diameter, and they are thought to assist absorption of water and solutes by providing a greatly increased surface area. The function of the invaginations seems to be related to secretion and excretion, as well as to absorption. Substances to be extruded from cells accumulate in vesicles lined with unit membrane; the vesicle moves to the surface and comes into contact with the plasma membrane; the two membranes fuse, the vesicle becomes an invagination, and the contents are passed to the exterior. Clearly observable forms of absorption are pinocytosis (engulfment of water and solutes) and phagocytosis (engulfment of solid particles); an invagination, which is small in pinocytosis and large in phagocytosis, forms about the material to be engulfed, the lips of the cavity come together and fuse, and the vesicle thus produced moves inward away from the surface.

Extraneous coat

The boundary between a cell and its environment should not be thought of as a sharp line of demarcation at the outer surface of the plasma membrane (or even at the outer surface of the bacterial cell wall or the thick additional membranes that occur about many animal eggs). Cell components exist also beyond these structures, though naturally in concentrations that fall rapidly with increasing distance from the cell. These components exist partly as substances suspended in the surrounding medium, but to varying degrees they also constitute a stable viscous layer that is capable of influencing relations between cell and environment. The viscous layer is maintained in a state of dynamic equilibrium, the continuous losses that occur being made good by regeneration from the cell. Where such extraneous coats exist in sufficient bulk to permit isolation and chemical study, they are found to consist chiefly of mucoprotein. This is also the composition of the animal egg membranes just referred to, which could with some reason be regarded as specialized forms of extraneous coat.

Cell wall

The cell wall is characteristically a feature of plants, including bacteria. It provides protection and support to the cell, but precludes the entry of food materials in the solid state. Animal cells can engulf solid particles, but plant cells must absorb their nutrients in solution. The bacterial cell wall is made up of protein-lipide-polysaccharide complexes, while that of most plants is composed mainly of cellulose, hemicellulose, and compounds of pectic acid. When a bacterium divides, cytoplasmic cleavage follows nuclear division, and a transverse cell wall, continuous with the outer cell wall, grows in to make a complete partition. Then the transverse wall splits into two layers, thus separating the two daughter cells. When a typical plant cell undergoes division, local thickenings appear in the equatorial plane of the telophase spindle, and these develop into a fine, double cell plate, the middle lamella, which transects the whole cell. The middle lamella consists of pectic substances when first formed, but is later reinforced by the deposition of celluloses. Continuity may be retained between the cytoplasm of the two daughter cells by perforations in the intervening wall.

Cell contact

Over the area of contact between cells in animal tissues, the plasma membranes are in close approximation, being separated usually by a distance of 100 to 150 Å. The material occupying the intervening space is spoken of as cement substance or gap substance and is presumably to be identified with the extraneous coat material. Treatment of cells with hypertonic glucose solution can permit the plasma membranes to approach to within 10 Å, evidently by withdrawing water from the gap substance. Closeness of approach of this order can also occur between regions of cell surfaces having radii of curvature of about $0.1\ \mu$. At a distance of rather less than 10 Å, it is possible that ionic bonding, involving bivalent ions such as Ca^{++}, can be established. Over greater distances, longer range forces are necessarily responsible for cell adhesion.

Studies made in tissue culture have shown that cells are responsive to structural features of the surfaces with which they come in contact—a phenomenon known as contact guidance. It is thought that this is one of the means whereby cells become orientated in tissues. A mechanism that is similar but of a rather different order of magnitude may also be involved in the high degree of specificity that marks the formation of stable associations between cells, the specificity being possibly conferred by the pattern of molecular configurations at the cell surface. Both species and organ specificity are demonstrable.

Another form of behavior in cells in tissue culture is referred to as contact inhibition. This term denotes the consequences seen when two normal tissue cells meet—their forward movement promptly ceases, and they form a temporary though stable region of attachment along their surfaces in contact. By contrast, tumor cells or those that have undergone malignant transformation do not show contact inhibition and glide past or over cells they meet—behavior that could underlie the invasiveness of tumor cells in tissues.

Mitosis and cell cleavage

When a cell divides into two daughter cells, division of the nucleus precedes division of the cytoplasm. Nuclear division is almost always effected by mitosis; amitosis seems restricted to somatic cells in insects, to cells in certain pathological tissues, and possibly to some Protista. The prophase of mitosis begins with the condensation and assembly of the chromosomes, which have already undergone replication, and with concomitant disappearance of the nuclear membrane and nucleoli. At the same time, too, the centrioles separate and move round to opposite poles of the nucleus, while asters develop about them. (In plants, mitosis is typically anastral, and centrosomes are rarely seen.) With the advent of metaphase, the chromosomes become arranged at the equator of the spindle that develops between the asters; in anaphase, the centromeres divide, and the chromosome halves are drawn toward opposite poles of the spindle. Telophase begins as the chromosome groups reach the spindle poles, and the cell body now elongates in the long axis of the spindle. The cell surface dips in around the spindle equator, and cytoplasmic division is completed by deepening of the cleavage furrow. Telophase ends when the chromosomes resume the extended state and the nuclear membrane and nucleoli reappear.

Replication of chromosomes begins during interphase, the extra DNA being elaborated from cytoplasmic precursors. Histochemical and spectrophotomicrographic studies have shown that the DNA content of nuclei is doubled before the start of a mitosis; moreover, when the chromosomes first become visible, they can often be seen to consist of two halves (chromatids), but they behave and remain recognized as single chromosomes until the actual separation to spindle poles. In the first half of mitosis, the chromosomes not only condense but also increase in bulk, so that when the chromatids separate they immediately achieve the status of chromosomes, for they have acquired a volume comparable to that of the chromosomes when first condensed. For these reasons, in the late interphase and the first half of mitosis, the cell is said to be tetraploid in respect to DNA and diploid in respect of chromosome number—the newly formed daughter cells being diploid in both respects.

The factors involved in cytoplasmic cleavage have not yet been properly identified, and there has been much speculation on the origin and mechanism of development of the cleavage furrow. Most cells tend to assume a more or less spherical form preliminary to cleavage (unless already spherical, as are the eggs of many animals), and the cortex, which may be defined as a region of the cell adjacent to the plasma membrane, becomes progressively stiffer as though extra material were being incorporated in it. The suggestion has been made that the material in question derives from the telophase chromosome groups and that its incorporation leads eventually to a buckling-in of the cell surface. The furrow originates in the cortex immediately peripheral to the equator of the spindle; this is attributed to an influence emanating from the spindle. The deepening of the cleavage furrow involves actual growth of the cortex in this region, which continues until cleavage is complete. The longitudinal thrust of the spindle in the telophase separation of the chromosomes may well aid the initial parting of the daughter cells.

Meiosis

Through meiosis, which occurs at different points in the life cycle in different groups of organisms, the chromosome number and DNA content of cells is halved. Meiosis follows much the same pattern in the higher animals and plants, and involves two nuclear divisions: in the first, the chromosomes separate, and in the second, the centromeres and chromatids divide. Generally, the second metaphase follows directly upon the first telophase, but in a comparatively few species an interphase nucleus is formed, and this is then succeeded by a second prophase.

The prophase of the first meiotic division is notably prolonged; during this phase, the chromosomes aggregate in homologous pairs, or bivalents, corresponding regions of paternal and maternal chromosomes becoming arranged in close apposition. By this time, each chromosome consists of two chromatids, which are separate entities though they lie close beside each other and are held together by a common centromere. It is then that crossing over occurs, in which corresponding regions of chromosomes are exchanged: two of the four chromatids that make up a bivalent (one from each chromosome) break at precisely the same point, and each becomes united with the part exchanged with the other chromatid. For a short time after crossing over is completed, homologous chromosomes tend to remain attached at the points of interchange, thus forming the chiasmata; the number of chiasmata per chromosome (equal to the number of points of crossing over) varies from one to ten, or even more in some species (though rarely more than five in man).

In the first metaphase, the bivalents arrange themselves at the equator of the spindle, with their centromeres a short distance above and below this plane. At anaphase, the centromeres move toward corresponding poles of the spindle, taking with them whole chromosomes (as distinct from the half chromosomes that separate in mitosis), but of course, as a result of crossing over, these differ from the maternal and paternal chromosomes that came together in early prophase. The chromosome groups move to the poles of the spindle, which simultaneously elongates, until the full telophase separation is achieved. The second metaphase, anaphase, and telophase resemble the corresponding stages in mitosis, except that a haploid number of chromosomes is involved in the second meiotic division.

Two

Significance of Fertilization

Fertilization is so widely associated with the process of reproduction that there is a tendency to regard its function as one of promoting the multiplication of individuals. However, the immediate effect of fertilization, involving as it does the union of two cells, is a reduction in number; multiplication requires the division of successive generations of cells, and this occurs almost entirely by mitosis. Fertilization is in fact one of a series of nuclear changes that are part of the machinery of adaptive variation and the evolution of species. When it entails union of chromosome groups from unrelated sources, fertilization has in addition the special function of integration within the group or population. The significance of fertilization, and of the related nuclear changes, is best brought out by considering the effects produced when these are associated in various ways with mitotic cell division.

Multiplication

That organisms depend upon a succession of mitotic cell divisions for their multiplication is most evident among the Protista. Fission may be binary or multiple; binary fission takes place by cleavage of the cell body immediately after mitosis (or endomitosis); in multiple fission, the nucleus divides several times within the cell body, and the cytoplasm fragments terminally. Multiple fission may take the form of schizogony, when a number of new active individuals are produced, or of sporogony, when the result is a host of usually dormant spores. Spore formation as the chief method of proliferation is found also in

15

moderately complex plants, as in the Bryophyta and Pteridophyta. The dependence of multiplication on mitosis is less obvious among the Spermatophyta and Metazoa; the potentiality for increase, however, is clearly determined by the numbers of germ-cell precursors developed, and these multiply mitotically.

Multicellular organisms also exploit mitotic cell division in another way—by vegetative reproduction. In the lichens, small specialized structures called soredia, consisting of a few fungal hyphae enclosing several algae, are separated from the parent plant and, after distribution by wind or rain, establish new lichen plants in suitable regions. In the angiosperms, vegetative reproduction is seen in the development of runners, suckers, bulbils, rhizomes, and tubers. Less common mechanisms are apogamy and nucellar embryony—the development of sporophytes from gametophyte cells other than the oösphere (i.e., the synergidae or antipodal cells) or from the nucellar cells; and apospory—the development of gametophytes from nucellar or integumental cells.

Many members of the Metazoa employ the vegetative method. Sea anemones may detach small portions of the main body as they move over rock surfaces, and these fragments grow into new adult individuals. Coelenterates and some echinoderms are capable of undergoing vertical fission, in a manner resembling that shown by certain highly specialized

a

Fig. 2.1.   Successive stages in the process of vertical fission, as shown by (a) *Vorticella*, and (b) a polyp (view of oral disc). Redrawn from Agassiz and Gould, *Principles of Zoology*, 1857.

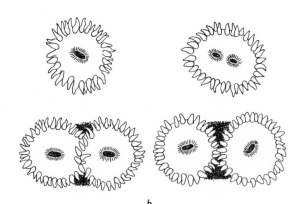

b

protozoa, each half becoming a whole animal (it is by this means that sea anemones and starfish appear to "pull themselves in two") (Fig. 2.1). Some metazoans can also reproduce vegetatively by budding. This may be effected by the aggregation of some of the cells into specialized, circumscribed structures which, like bacterial spores, can survive conditions that would normally be lethal, giving rise to new individuals when a favorable environment is restored. Such structures are known as gemmules in sponges and statoblasts in bryozoans. In other instances, the new individual develops like a neoplasm on the body of the parent animal and later becomes separated; this is seen in bryozoans, coelenterates, polychaetes, cestodes and even in so high a group as ascidians. Alternatively, the new individuals may remain attached and so form a colony. Budding in ascidians also takes place from outgrowths called stolons, analogous to the branches of a hydrozoan colony on which the polyps develop.

Allied to budding in Metazoa is polyembryony, by means of which a single egg can give rise to more than one embryo. The eggs of some parasitic Hymenoptera each produce a hundred or more larvae by multiple division of the original fertilized cell. Polyembryony is probably the mechanism whereby rediae and cercariae arise in the life cycle of the liver fluke, *Fasciola hepatica:* they all appear to develop from descendants of the propagative cell formed at the first cleavage division of the fertilized egg (Fig. 2.2). In some Bryozoa, the egg forms a primary embryo from which small masses of cells are nipped off to differentiate into secondary embryos, each of which becomes a free-swimming larva. Several species of mammals also exhibit polyembryony (monovular twins, triplets, etc.), including the opossum, cow, sheep, and pig, as well, of course, as man. The condition is especially well developed in certain armadillos: *Dasypus novemcinctus* regularly produces litters of identical quadruplets (Fig. 2.3), while in *D. hybridus* the number of monovular young ranges from eight to twelve. In *D. novemcinctus*, the first signs of plurality appear soon after gastrulation, when segregation of embryonic ectoderm occurs: first, two invaginations of the ectodermic vesicle appear, then four. In *D. hybridus*, segregation is later, in the primitive streak stage. Polyembryony occurs also in some plants, e.g., *Pinus*, where the fertilized oösphere divides into two or more pro-embryos.

Many unicellular organisms can maintain continuity and increase for prolonged periods by an uninterrupted series of mitotic cell divisions. Multiplication of this kind is highly efficient, for all the cells of each generation can play a direct role in it, and organisms that employ it can most effectively exploit their environment. This form of reproduction, however, tends to perpetuate uniformity—each generation is

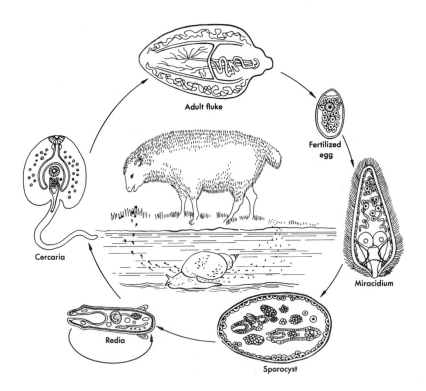

Fig. 2.2.   The life cycle of *Fasciola hepatica*, the liver fluke of sheep. The adult fluke is hermaphrodite, but fertilization is normally heterologous. The fertilized eggs hatch into miracidia, which
metamorphose into sporocysts in the pond snail. Within the sporocysts develop rediae, and these
in turn give rise to further rediae over several generations. Finally rediae produce cercariae,
which leave the pond snail and, entering a sheep, grow into liver flukes. Generation of rediae
and cercariae is considered to take place by a form of polyembryony and not parthenogenesis.

identical to the previous one, and the resultant population is quite
homogeneous. Lack of variation means that the capacity for adaptation
is strictly limited, and the organisms depend heavily on the stability
of the environment. If conditions change, the population is in danger
of dying out unless special defensive mechanisms such as encystment
or spore formation are available to give protection until a favorable
environment is restored.

Variations do appear in populations maintained by uncomplicated
mitotic divisions, however, and they are attributable to mutations.
These are rare events, and the great majority are unfavorable and
usually lethal to the individuals in which they appear; but every now
and then a mutation confers a definite advantage, enabling the organism

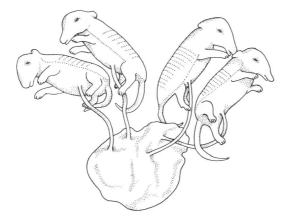

Fig. 2.3. Advanced fetuses—uniovular quadruplets—of the armadillo *Dasypus novemcinctus.*

to succeed where it would otherwise have failed. When advantageous mutations occur, new groups of organisms are founded and flourish under the conditions for which they are peculiarly fitted. In this way successful genotypes tend to be stabilized, but as each is established the original population becomes progressively subdivided. The effect of mutation, therefore, is gradually to break up the population into an increasing number of biotypes which will continue to diverge in character in the course of evolution as one mutation after another is incorporated in the different lines of descent.

A continuous succession of mitotic cell divisions clearly has serious deficiencies as a means for the maintenance and advancement of a race, and reproduction, in almost all groups of living organisms, involves nuclear changes in addition to mitosis. The most important of these is meiosis, which is very widespread in its occurrence and may be universal. The periodic interpolation of meiosis or meiosis-like changes into a series of mitotic cell divisions characterizes the reproductive pattern of organisms that multiply parthenogenetically.

Meiosis in parthenogenesis

Parthenogenesis involving partial or complete development is known in representatives of many groups of animals, including coelenterates, rotifers, platyhelminths, nematodes, annelids, molluscs, crustaceans, myriapods, insects, arachnids, fishes, amphibians, birds, and mammals. It also occurs in certain angiosperms such as lady's-mantle

(*Alchemilla*), meadow rue (*Thalictrum*), dandelion (*Taraxacum*) and hawkweed (*Hieracium*), which as a result produce seeds without fertilization. Parthenogenesis in the vast majority of instances is initiated in female gametes, though it can arise in male gametes in algae that exhibit isogamy or anisogamy. Parthenogenesis can be natural or artificial; artificial parthenogenesis is provoked by stimulation of the eggs with chemical or physical agents. Development in parthenogenesis may lead to the production of males (arrhenotoky) or females (thelytoky), or sometimes both (deuterotoky or amphotoky).

Far-going parthenogenetic development appears to be essentially a nonmammalian feature. There is no certain evidence of the birth of a natural parthenogenone in any mammal; in rabbits, which have been used most widely as experimental animals, artificially activated eggs rarely advance to implantation, and conclusive evidence is lacking that much further development has ever occurred. Among birds, the best authenticated cases of natural parthenogenesis are in turkeys; up to 80 per cent of eggs have been found on incubation to show some signs of cleavage, and very occasionally development proceeds to hatching and even to maturity. All the turkey parthenogenones investigated have been males. Some of the earliest experiments on the artificial induction of parthenogenetic development were made on frog eggs; when pricked with a needle bearing traces of blood, these eggs, though unfertilized, sometimes developed to mature frogs.

The regular occurrence of natural parthenogenesis is evidently restricted to the invertebrates. Arrhenotoky is well shown in the Hymenoptera, in most of which haploid males derive from unfertilized eggs and diploid females from fertilized ones (as in the honeybee *Apis mellifera*). Spermatogenesis is ameiotic in these forms. Thelytoky is seen in two widely practised systems—namely, paedogenesis and cyclic parthenogenesis. These characterize the reproductive patterns of some animals during periods of rapid multiplication that occur when the environment is favorable; with the advent of overcrowding, cold, drought, or food shortage, sexual reproduction (involving fertilization) is adopted, and "resting" eggs are laid that remain dormant until the environment becomes favorable once more. Paedogenesis is found in gall flies and midges; larvae of the gall fly *Miastor metraolas*, for example, hatch from fertilized eggs, and after a short period of growth, but before metamorphosis, give rise to new larvae that are born viviparously. Germ cells within the larvae undergo precocious maturation, without chromosome reduction, and develop parthenogenetically into larvae that parasitize and eventually consume the mother larva. Successive generations of paedogenetic larvae are produced while conditions remain favorable. When change occurs, larvae of a new kind are formed, and these, after pupating, give rise to the adult male and female gall flies.

Mating takes place, and fertilized eggs are laid that will eventually yield the paedogenetic larvae of the next cycle.

Basically, the same sort of thing happens in cyclic parthenogenesis, which is seen among the rotifers, water fleas, aphids, and gall wasps, the main difference being that successive generations hatch from eggs laid, rather than from the "internal" eggs of larvae. In the aphid *Tetraneura ulmi*, female nymphs hatch from fertilized eggs, become

Fig. 2.4. Life cycle of the aphid *Tetraneura ulmi*. Eggs that have lain dormant over winter hatch in the spring yielding wingless forms, the Fundatrices, which form galls wherein they lay the eggs that give rise to the winged Emigrantes. These individuals make their way out of the galls and seek out the roots of various grasses, there to lay eggs that hatch into wingless Exules. Several successive generations of Exules follow; then, in late summer, eggs are laid from which the winged Sexuparae emerge, and these fly back to elm trees where male- and female-producing eggs are deposited. The males and females of the next generation, the Sexuales, mate and lay the eggs that pass through the winter period. The individuals of all generations except the Fundatrices are parthenogenones, the eggs undergoing a single nonreductional maturation division. Male Sexuales (XO) arise through loss of an X chromosome in the maturation division.

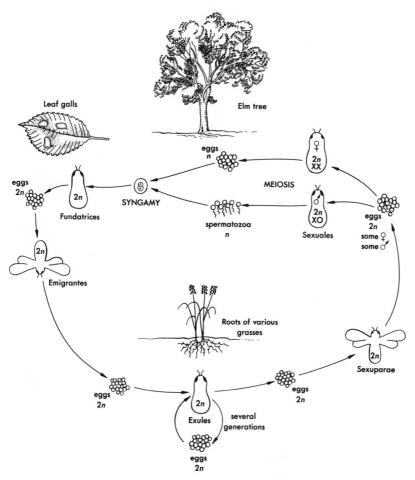

adult, and lay eggs that develop parthenogenetically into winged forms; these migrate to other plants, on which several further parthenogenetic generations follow. Finally, male and female aphids are formed, again by parthenogenesis, mating takes place, and fertilized eggs are laid (Fig. 2.4).

Meiosis in the alternation of generations

In plants, a regular alternation of diploid (sporophyte) and haploid (gametophyte) generations is discernible, meiosis being involved in spore formation and mitosis in gametogenesis (except in some algae, such as *Fucus*, where meiosis takes place in gametogenesis). Thus, in the alga *Enteromorpha intestinalis*, the gametophytes are haploid, and the zygotes give rise to diploid sporophytes which, through meiosis, produce haploid spores. Germination of the spores yields the gametophyte (*n*) stage again. In this species, sporophyte and gametophyte are morphologically identical, so that *E. intestinalis* provides an example

Fig. 2.5. Life cycle of the brown alga *Cutleria-Aglaozonia*, which shows anisogamy and pronounced antithetic alternation of generations. Meiosis occurs in spore formation.

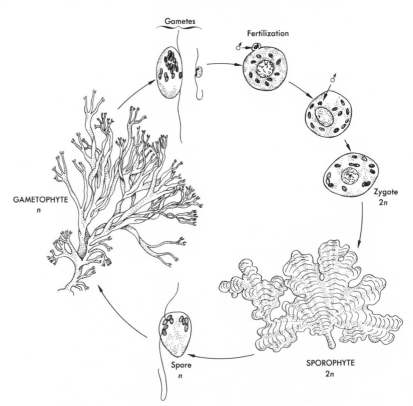

Gametes

Fertilization

Zygote
2n

GAMETOPHYTE
n

Spore
n

SPOROPHYTE
2n

of isomorphic or homologous alternation of generations. Another alga, *Cutleria-Aglaozonia*, displays heteromorphic or antithetic alternation of generations; here, plants of the diploid sporophytic generation are very different from those of the haploid gametophytic generation (Fig. 2.5). In higher plants, antithetic alternation is the more common. The well-known form of the moss plant *Funaria* is the gametophyte (n); fertilization of the oösphere leads to the growth, parasitically on the gametophyte, of a single aerial stem which is the sporophyte ($2n$). The reverse form of antithetic alternation is found in the Pteridophyta and Spermatophyta, where the sporophyte is the principal stage and the gametophyte is reduced to a diminutive structure (Fig. 2.6). In Spermatophyta, the male gametophyte is represented by the pollen tube with its nuclei and the female by the nucellus and ovule.

Alternation of generations also occurs in some members of the animal kingdom, though the alternation relates rather to the type of devel-

Fig. 2.6. Life cycle of a fern. (a) Meiosis takes place during spore formation in the sporangia of the diploid sporophyte. (b) The spores germinate and produce a diminutive haploid prothallus (gametophyte) on which develop antheridia ($\male$) and archegonia ($\female$). (c) On release, the spermatozoids are attracted by chemical substances (L-malic acid in *Pteridium*) secreted by the canal cells of the archegonium. Fertilization of the egg leads to development of diploid zygote and the new sporophyte.

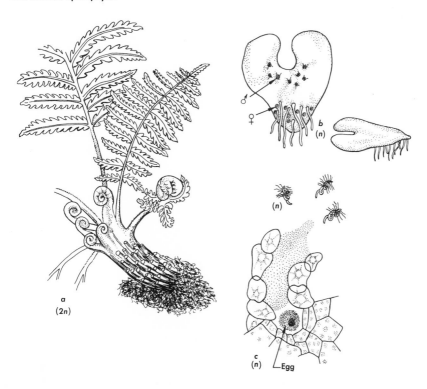

opment (vegetative on the one hand, and parthenogenetic or sexual on the other) than to the existence of haploidy or diploidy. In *Plasmodium*, the causal organism of malaria, meiosis is involved in gametogenesis, which is followed by syngamy and polyembryony (sporogony); all this takes place in the body of the vector mosquito, and alternates with events that occur in the human blood stream wherein reproduction is by multiple fission (schizogony) (Fig. 2.7). In the jellyfish *Aurelia*, the medusae constitute the sexual generation; planula larvae hatching from the fertilized eggs become sessile hydratubae which give rise vegetatively to new hydratubae or bud off ephyra larvae, and the latter develop into adult medusae. In the polychaete worm *Autolytus cornutus*, the asexual forms arising from fertilized eggs bud off a succession of sexual zooids that eventually become functional male and female worms. Alternation of generations is well shown also in insects in the processes of paedogenesis (e.g., *Miastor metraolas*) and cyclic parthenogenesis (e.g., *Tetraneura ulmi*).

Role of meiosis

Meiosis almost always entails, through the occurrence of crossing over, a redistribution of genes between homologous chromosomes (except, for example, in the spermatogenesis of many Diptera), so that the resultant four chromosome groups differ from one another and from the mother nucleus. Meiosis thus provides considerable reassortment of genetic factors; it goes far to counteract the uniformity associated with mitosis, and enhances the possibilities of adaptation to changing environments. But of course no new genes are introduced, and so the daughter nuclei cannot exhibit genes that were not in the mother nucleus, unless mutation intervenes. In addition, the lack of means for the interchange of favorable genes between clones of organisms signifies that meiosis does nothing to prevent the divergent development of biotypes inherent in vegetative reproduction. Characteristically, parthenogenetic individuals prosper in specific biological niches; changes threaten their extinction, unless they are capable of adopting a mode of reproduction involving the introduction of new genes by recombination from different sources. In nature, few if any species reproduce exclusively parthenogenetically; probably all employ at one time or another the device of gene recombination.

As a result of meiosis, the chromosome number is reduced by half, and accordingly, except in the case of male haploidy in insects, there occurs in addition a complementary change leading to restoration of the former state of ploidy. The mechanism that underlies fertilization and is responsible for the recombination of genes from different sources seems to have developed naturally from one of these corrective nuclear

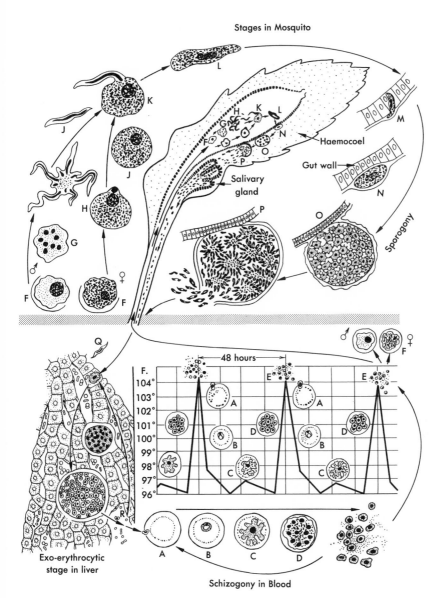

Stages in Mosquito

Haemocoel

Gut wall

Salivary gland

Sporogony

48 hours

Exo-erythrocytic stage in liver

Schizogony in Blood

Fig. 2.7. Life cycle of the malaria parasite *Plasmodium vivax*. (a to e) Stages of the erythrocyte infestation—in which multiple fission (schizogony) occurs—and the course of the febrile response in the patient. (f to l) Gametogenesis, heterogamic fertilization and formation of zygote while the parasite is within the gut of the mosquito. (m to p) The phase of polyembryony (sporogony) in the wall of the gut. (q and r) The phase of multiple fission in the liver of the human host. Redrawn from W. F. Wheeler, *Intermediate Biology*, 6th ed. (Heinemann, 1962).

changes; it is appropriate therefore that they should receive attention before consideration is given to the nature and effects of syngamy.

Restoration of the chromosome number

Restoration takes place in a variety of ways. In some earthworms and planarians, doubling of the chromosome number occurs before meiosis (in the final oögonial division or in the prophase of meiosis), so that adjustment is in effect brought about by meiosis itself. In some algae, such as *Oedogonium*, meiosis replaces mitosis in the first two cleavages of the zygote, giving rise to four new individuals (zygotic meiosis). By one means or another the separation of chromosomes in either the first or the second meiotic division may be suppressed. In the moth *Solenobia lichenella*, the first anaphase fails soon after separation begins and the two chromosome groups reunite, so that the second meiotic division takes place with double the number of chromosomes. In another moth, *Apterona helix*, after anaphase failure and chromosome reunion, the second meiotic division functions as the first cleavage division[1]; here no polar groups are formed at all. In the brine shrimp *Artemia salina*, it is the second meiotic division that is suppressed, and this happens after centromere division but before effective chromosome separation. Restoration after the second meiotic division is found in the process of autogamy in *Paramecium;* the two nuclei left after the completion of meiosis fuse, and the cell divides into two daughter cells which then regain their normal nuclear complement (Fig. 5.22). In some eggs of the silk moth *Bombyx mori*, and apparently also in artificially activated frog eggs, the first cleavage mitosis is inhibited in early anaphase, and the two sets of chromosomes are incorporated in a single nucleus which is later divided by a normal second cleavage division. In the moth *Solenobia triquetrella*, the first and second cleavage divisions take place with the reduced number of chromosomes, and restoration occurs through fusion in pairs of the resulting four nuclei. There are also some animals in which (in their parthenogenetic phase) meiosis is completely suppressed: the mollusc *Campeloma*, the crustaceans *Trichoniscus* and *Daphnia*, and the insects *Saga* and *Tetraneura*.

---

[1] This curious change in the role of a maturation spindle has been provoked experimentally in some animals. Treatment of the egg of the echiuroid worm *Urechis caupo* with hypotonic sea water often results in a shift of the first maturation spindle, which takes the position normally occupied by the first cleavage spindle (in the center of the egg and at right angles to the polar axis). Division then results in cleavage of the whole egg, despite the fact that the chromosomes are still as bivalents and in haploid number. (Similar behavior of a maturation spindle is known in mouse eggs—see "Partial fertilization" in Chapter 7.)

Syngamy and its consequences

The most characteristic feature of fertilization is the syngamy or union of gamete nuclei, but examination shows that there is no hard and fast line of demarcation between syngamy in sexual reproduction and the method of restoration of chromosome number in parthenogenesis involving reunion of nuclei formed by the second meiotic division. Several intermediate steps can be identified: the first is represented by the process of autogamy as it occurs in several Protozoa, such as *Actinophrys sol.* After a succession of mitotic divisions, the organism forms a cyst, within which it divides into two cells. The nucleus of each daughter cell then undergoes two meiotic divisions, after which the cells unite and their nuclei fuse. The organism emerges from the cyst and begins another period of multiplication by mitosis. It hardly seems possible that autogamy could confer any advantage additional to those deriving from meiosis coupled with restoration of diploidy; yet there is something curiously like conjugation in the way in which the daughter cells unite, one cell becoming the more mobile and actively invading the other. Not far removed is endogamy, which is displayed, for example, by *Paramecium aurelia;* the descendants of a single cell after only eight or nine divisions may conjugate, despite the fact that they must have identical genetic constitutions unless mutation has occurred.

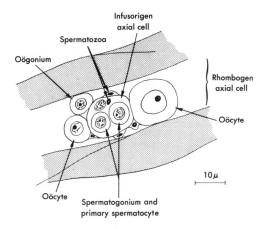

Fig. 2.8. Gametogenesis and fertilization in the mesozoan *Dicyema*. A single cell lying in the axial cell of the parent organism (rhombogen) gives rise directly to the oögonium and to the infusorigen axial cell. From the oögonium a series of oöcytes is produced, and within the infusorigen axial cell spermatozoa arise which emerge to fertilize the oöcytes. The organism is thus a self-fertilizing hermaphrodite producing heterogamous gametes. Redrawn from C. R. Austin, *Parasitology*, 54 (1964), 597.

Analogous to endogamy is the self-fertilization of higher plants (in which it is often referred to as autogamy) and of mesozoan (Fig. 2.8) and metazoan hermaphrodites. Often there is a bar to self-fertilization, as in ascidians such as *Ciona*, but in certain cestodes, nematodes, and molluscs, self-fertilization is evidently the usual event. Even among the vertebrates, there are a few examples of this state of affairs: in teleost fish of the genera *Serranus* and *Sargus*, mature eggs and spermatozoa are shed at the same time by the one individual, and there seems little doubt that fertilization often involves autologous gametes.

Syngamy, therefore, does not in itself appear to constitute any advance over other methods of regulation to diploidy. It is only when nuclei from relatively unrelated cells take part in syngamy that a new feature becomes evident—namely, the recombination of genes from different sources. This is the big step forward: it makes possible the dissemination of advantageous genes throughout a group, population, or race, where before they were restricted to the clone, and provides an integrating effect that counteracts the tendency to divergent development of biotypes. The peculiar function of heterologous syngamy is integration, and the effect is clearly greater with more distantly related genotypes.

In the exercise of its integrating influence, heterologous syngamy appears to be part of a more general and perhaps universal phenomenon, as yet rather inadequately understood, for there are several other mechanisms, differing in many respects from syngamy, that also involve dissemination of genes throughout a group or population. These are best known in the bacteria. Thus, cells that have survived infection by bacteriophage often show new characteristics that can be identified as those of bacteria previously infected with the same phages. These qualities are passed on to the descendants of the recipient organism as heritable characters, and the underlying genetic factors become, in fact, genes on the bacterial chromosome. The process involves the transport by the virus of genetic information, coded in DNA molecules, from one bacterium to another and is known as transduction. The effect can be duplicated artificially by treating a culture of bacteria with a cell-free extract prepared from other bacteria possessing distinguishably different characteristics—the treated organisms acquire features that become part of their heritable make-up. This is known as transformation; it also depends on the transmission of genes in the form of molecular aggregates of DNA. There is evidence, too, that transformation can occur naturally: genes released from bacteria that die and undergo lysis can be taken up by other bacteria living in the same medium. It is tempting to suppose that something analogous to transduction can also occur in complex organisms, through the agency of pathogenic viruses, and perhaps even of viruses as yet undetected because they lack pathogenic effect, but these ideas currently need experimental support.

The significance of fertilization can be seen to depend upon the relationship that exists between the sources of the chromosome complements taking part in syngamy. With the closest relationship, fertilization does little if any more than restore the diploid state—an effect that it shares with other nuclear changes. As the relationship becomes more distant, a new element enters—the dissemination of genes throughout the group or population; this aids in the adaptive variation of the race, and it also introduces the integrating influence so clearly lacking from other reproductive mechanisms. Fertilization finally emerges as part of a generalized system of gene dispersal, the full influence of which is as yet but vaguely understood.

THREE

Form and Differentiation
of Gametes

In many single-celled organisms, the gametes differ little in size or
structure from the adult vegetative individuals, and this relationship
is known as hologamy. In other members of the Protista, the gametes
are smaller, often much smaller, than the vegetative parent cell, the
size difference being related to the number of cell divisions involved in
gamete formation; they also show structural differences from the vegetative cells and are usually motile. Such a relationship is termed
merogamy. Among both hologamous and merogamous gametes, any
one of three relationships can exist: the conjugants may be strikingly
similar to each other in form (isogamy), slightly different (anisogamy),
or very different (heterogamy). Definition of these categories is not
rigid: in the single-celled alga *Clamydomonas*, isogamy and anisogamy
are shown by different strains, and even by the same strain at different
times; in the fungus *Basidiobolus*, two identical mycelia come into
contact, but as the nucleus from one mycelium migrates to join that
in the other, the second mycelium enlarges greatly to form a bulbous
structure—here, an initial isogamy becomes a final anisogamy (Fig. 3.1).
In heterogamy, the smaller gamete (microgamete) is usually motile,
and the larger one (macrogamete) passive—features that characterize
spermatozoon and egg, respectively; but there are exceptions: in the
gregarine *Stylocephalus*, for example, the macrogamete is motile and the
microgamete passive (Fig. 3.2).

Isogamy is almost exclusively a morphological feature, for there is
evidence of functional difference between most isogamous gametes. It
has already been noted that the two structurally similar cells taking
part in autogamy in *Actinophrys* behave differently, one actively invad-

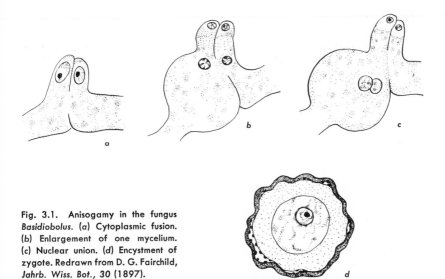

Fig. 3.1. Anisogamy in the fungus *Basidiobolus*. (a) Cytoplasmic fusion. (b) Enlargement of one mycelium. (c) Nuclear union. (d) Encystment of zygote. Redrawn from D. G. Fairchild, *Jahrb. Wiss. Bot.*, 30 (1897).

ing the other (see "Syngamy and its consequences" in Chapter 2). The active cell advances several fingerlike pseudopods toward its inactive partner, and these very likely have a special significance for fusion between the two cells (see "Cytoplasmic fusion" in Chapter 5). In *Trichonympha* there is isogamy, though conjugation is evidently between unrelated cells (exogamy); here too, one cell actively invades, seemingly piercing the other with its pointed rostrum. Functional differences are in fact more generally recognized by the occurrence of conjugation only between individuals of different parentage or between members of different mating types, and selective behavior of this kind is of wide incidence.

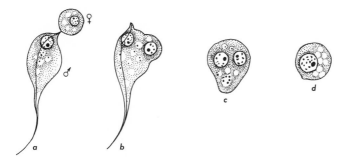

Fig. 3.2. Fertilization in the gregarine *Stylocephalus*, involving heterogamy in which the macrogamete is the motile one. Redrawn from Legér and Duboscq, *Arch. Protozoenk.*, *17* (1909).

Mating types

Conjugation in bacteria occurs between pairs of organisms of different mating types; these features have been studied particularly in strains of *Escherichia, Pseudomonas, Salmonella,* and *Shigella.* In *E. coli* it has been possible to identify three mating types, of which those designated F^+ (denoting fertility) and Hfr (denoting high frequency of recombination) are made up of donor cells; the type designated F^- contains the recipients. Genetic material passes only from donor to recipient and never in the reverse direction. The F^+ state is attributable to the possession by the bacterium of the sex factor, which is an autonomous, cytoplasmic element; at conjugation, only the sex factor is transferred, and the recipient in consequence is converted to a donor type. In *Hfr* cells, the sex factor behaves as an ordinary gene attached terminally on the bacterial chromosome; at conjugation, varying proportions of the chromosome are passed to the recipient cell, but the sex factor is very rarely transferred, and the recipient remains a member of the recipient type (Fig. 5.21). Sex factor resembles a bacteriophage in several respects.

More complex patterns of mating types are known and have been extensively studied in the ciliates. Most attention has been given to *Paramecium,* where there are two kinds of systems: in one, exemplified by *P. aurelia, P. caudatum, P. woodruffi,* and *P. calkinsi,* species are made up of varieties with only two mating types each; in the other system, exemplified by *P. bursaria, P. trichum,* and *P. multimicronucleatum,* some of the varieties contain several mating types. In *P. aurelia,* eight varieties have been recognized, each containing two mating types, and one variety with only one mating type (type XIII). As a rule, individuals of any one mating type will not mate with each other, but only with members of the other mating type in the same variety; exceptionally, intervarietal mating does occur, though the reaction is not as intense as with intravarietal mating and seldom leads to complete conjugation. Type XIII must necessarily mate intervarietally and this it does with members of types II, V, and X. In *P. caudatum,* there appears to be even greater complexity, with thirteen varieties and twenty-five mating types (variety 10 having only one mating type). Where several mating types make up a variety, as in the second group of organisms, mating occurs freely between the various mating types, but intervarietal mating is again rare. In *P. bursaria,* three varieties each contain four mating types, and one variety contains eight. The high specificity of mating-type reactions seen in *Paramecium* is evidently attributable to the presence of mating-type substances attached to the surface of the animals, or to the molecular pattern of the surface structure (see "Cell contact" in Chapter 1).

In another ciliate, *Euplotes patella*, a pattern of mating types comparable to that in *Paramecium* has been demonstrated, and evidence for the existence of mating types has also been found in *Leucophrys patula*, *Onychodromus grandis*, *Stylonichia pustulata*, *S. putrina*, *Lyxophyllum fasciola*, and *Euplotes herpa*, but the details have yet to be worked out.

More complex organisms also show mating-type phenomena. In some species of *Spirogyra*, for example, conjugation (involving migration of cells from one filament into another) occurs only between members of different filaments; moreover, all the cells of some filaments prove to be migratory or "male," while all those of other filaments are passive or "female." Then again, it has been found that in some fungi, such as *Mucor mucedo* and *Rhizopus nigricans*, two kind of mycelia exist, which are designated + and −. The isogamous gametes produced by these mycelia will only conjugate + to − or − to +. If the two strains of mycelia are kept separate, reproduction proceeds parthenogenetically for many generations, and conjugation is resumed only when they are brought together once more. These kinds of mating-type relationships foreshadow the clear-cut heterogamy that exists in most members of the plant and animal kingdoms, wherein specialized microgametes (antherozoids, spermatozoids, spermatozoa) and macrogametes (oöspheres, ova, eggs) have been developed.

Microgametes, antherozoids, spermatozoids, spermatozoa

The structure of microgametes differs widely. The great majority consist essentially of a nucleus accompanied by a much reduced amount of cytoplasm and mechanisms for motility, such as flagella or cilia. In addition, many possess an organelle; the acrosome, that enables the cell to traverse barriers that surround the corresponding macrogametes. Examples of some of the many patterns seen in microgametes are illustrated in Figs. 3.3–3.5. In Figs. 3.3 and 3.4, the nuclei are shown black and the cytoplasmic components white or stippled. Acrosomes appear to be lacking from the microgametes of plants, sporozoans, and some worms, such as certain turbellarians and *Ascaris*, though an acrosome has been described in the earthworm spermatozoon. Details of acrosome structure as ascertained by electron microscopy are depicted in Fig. 3.6.

The cytoplasmic components of many spermatozoa, possibly all, are known to include mitochondria. Flagella, on the other hand, are by no means universal: nonflagellate spermatozoa are produced by certain members of the nematodes, myriapods, crustaceans, and arachnids. Mesozoans, some nematodes (*Ascaris*), and crustaceans (*Polyphemus*) have amoeboid spermatozoa.

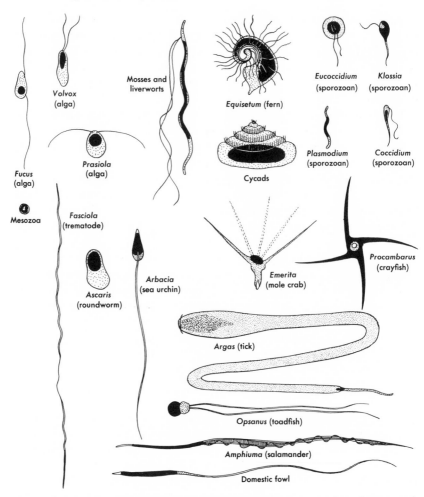

Fig. 3.3.   Forms of spermatozoa; nucleus in black. Spermatozoa similar to those of mosses and liverworts are found among the turbellarian flatworms.

Spermatozoa of sea urchin and rabbit

A detailed description of metazoan sperm morphology is conveniently based on two intensively studied types represented by the spermatozoa of the sea urchin *Arbacia punctulata* and the rabbit *Oryctolagus cuniculus* (Fig. 3.7). In each of these, the main structural subdivisions are into head, midpiece, and tail, the head being further divisible into acrosome, perforatorium, and nucleus. As with any other living cell, the spermatozoon is contained by a plasma membrane, on the integrity of which the life of the cell depends. There is also evidence of some form

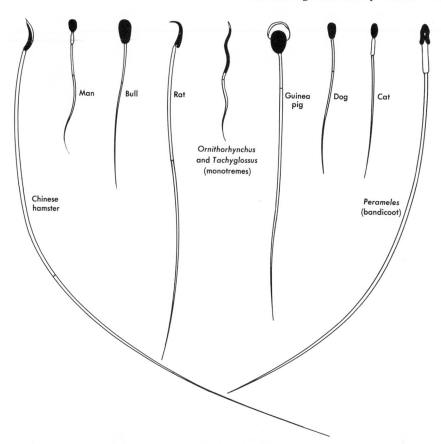

Fig. 3.4. Diagram of mammalian spermatozoa, to show relative sizes and variations in shape of head (nucleus black) and proportion of tail that is midpiece.

of extraneous coat, which is responsible for some of the antigenic properties of the spermatozoon, and probably also for the specificity of sperm-egg interaction, and which appears to confer stability to the acrosome, at least in mammalian spermatozoa (see "Acrosome reaction" in Chapter 5). Sea urchin spermatozoa have an over-all length of 45 μ, with a 3.25 μ head; rabbit spermatozoa are 60 to 70 μ long, with a head of from 8 to 10 μ.

The acrosome is disposed at the tip of the sperm head and is a baglike structure; the wall is unit membrane, and the contents appear relatively dense by electron microscopy. In the sea-urchin spermatozoon, the acrosome is rounded anteriorly and flattened posteriorly; in the rabbit, the acrosome appears as if molded over the anterior half of the nucleus, so that it forms a double-walled sac with its posterior margin running

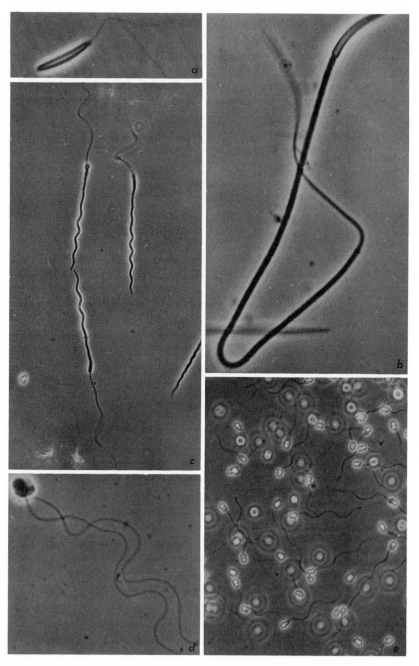

Fig. 3.5. Photographs of spermatozoa. (a) Frog, *Rana*, spermatozoon traversing the jelly coat of an egg. (b) Indigo snake, *Drymarchon*. (c) The electric ray, *Torpedo*. (d and e) The toadfish, *Opsanus* (see also Fig. 3.3). Pictures (c) and (e) are of actively motile spermatozoa; the frog spermatozoon (a) was just·moving; those shown in (b) and (d) were fixed.

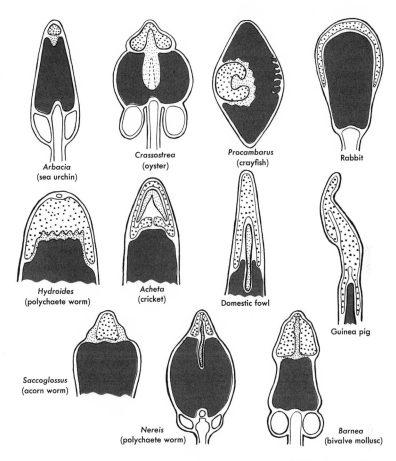

Fig. 3.6. Structure of the acrosome in various spermatozoa, as revealed by electron micrographic studies.

approximately along the equator of the nucleus. The acrosome almost certainly contains the egg-membrane lysins known to be carried by spermatozoa. It seems to be the least stable part of the spermatozoon; it sometimes "reacts" but more commonly breaks down (sea urchin) or becomes detached (rabbit) when the spermatozoon dies.

The term *perforatorium* has been used with several different meanings; among other things, it has been used by some authors to denote the entity here referred to as acrosome. The most logical application for the term would seem to be as a name for the structure lying between the acrosome and the nucleus, which has been shown in several animals to play an essential role in the penetration of the spermatozoon through egg investments (see "Acrosome reaction" in Chapter 5). In the sea urchin, the perforatorium as thus defined largely occupies the deep

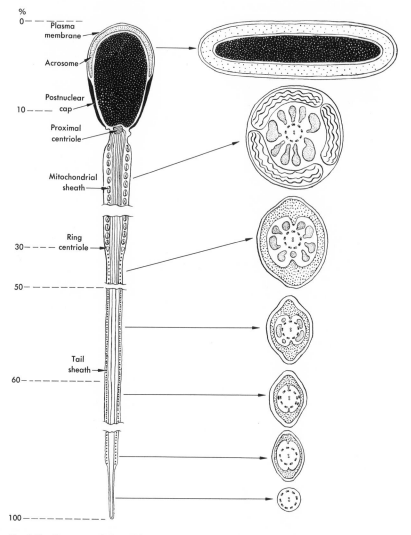

Fig. 3.7. Structure of the rabbit spermatozoon, as seen in vertical section and in a series of cross sections. The scale at the left shows proportions of total length.

indentation at the anterior pole of the nucleus and is involved in the formation of the acrosome filament. Extrusion of an acrosome filament—such a striking feature in many invertebrate spermatozoa—is not known in the rabbit, nor indeed in any mammal, but there are reasons for believing that some analogous form of reaction occurs, and that an as yet ill-defined region between acrosome and nucleus represents the rabbit perforatorium. Perforatoria of several animals are shown in Fig. 3.6.

The sperm nucleus consists chiefly of DNA-protein, in which the protein is primarily of the basic (histone) type, and it is limited by a nuclear membrane. In both sea urchin and rabbit, the components of the nucleus are so densely packed that a clear structural pattern cannot be distinguished; it is, however, logical to assume that the chromosomes are present in a form preserving the linear order of gene sequences. The shape of the nucleus is that of a truncated cone in sea-urchin spermatozoa, and of an oval disc in rabbit spermatozoa. In both species, the posterior pole of the nucleus has an indentation that accommodates the beginning of the tail.

The midpiece varies greatly in form in different animals. In the sea urchin, it is represented by a single mitochondrion arranged around the posterior aspect of the nucleus and encircling the tail. In the rabbit spermatozoon, the midpiece is that part of the tail that is surrounded by a tightly coiled spiral of elongated mitochondria; the term therefore includes the tail filaments and other components that are enclosed by the spiral. The mitochondrial spiral ends posteriorly at the ring centriole; this first appears in the spermatid in association with the proximal and distal centrioles which remain in the neck of the fully formed spermatozoon (Figs. 3.7 and 3.15). In view of the enzymic machinery carried by mitochondria, the midpiece is considered to be the region in which energy is made available for the motility of the tail. The energy can be derived from exogenous as well as endogenous substrates and through aerobic as well as anaerobic pathways (Fig. 3.8). Spermatozoa are thought to be capable also of limited anabolic activity (amino acid incorporation and lipid synthesis). These metabolic processes are not necessarily all limited to the mitochondria; indeed, some of the enzymes of the oxidative system have been demonstrated in the thick tail fibers, and there are suggestions that amino acid incorporation can occur in the acrosome.

The sperm tail begins with a specialized portion, the neck, by which it is inserted into the indentation in the posterior pole of the nucleus. The precise morphology of the neck is still uncertain; there is little doubt, however, that two centrioles (proximal and distal) are located here—though the structure of one or the other may be modified from that seen in somatic cells—and that they represent the origin of the fibrous elements of the tail (c.f. Fig. 3.9). In the sea-urchin spermatozoon, the tail fibers are arranged in a circle of nine with two more running down the middle—a pattern seen in cilia and flagella generally. Such an array of fibers is also seen in the rabbit sperm tail, where it is termed the *axial filament*. The rabbit sperm tail has in addition an outer ring of nine more fibers, much thicker than those of the inner ring (Figs. 3.7 and 3.10). The coarse fibers terminate one after another at various points down the tail, until only the axial filament remains. The fibers

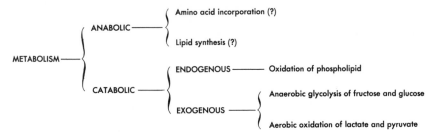

Fig. 3.8. Chief biochemical functions of mammalian spermatozoa.

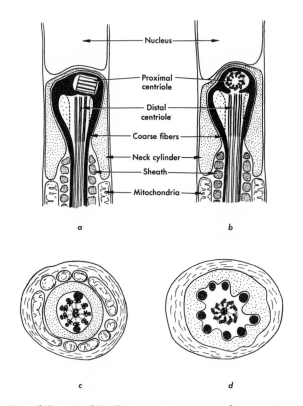

Fig. 3.9. Sections of the neck of the King snake spermatozoon (*Lampropeltis getulus*). (a) and (b) are vertical sections, (a) parallel to the long axis of the proximal centriole, and (b) at right angles to this axis. (c) and (d) are cross sections, (c) through the neck at a level about half way along the distal centriole, and (d) through the sperm tail a short distance below the neck. In (c), details of the distal centriole can be seen in the center, and this is surrounded by the coarse fibers deeply embedded in the neck cylinder. The typical $9 + 2$ pattern of the axial filament can be seen in the middle of the cross section in (d); the coarse fibers are much reduced in girth in this region, numbers 3 and 8 being the thickest. The two sets of tail fibers are enclosed by the thick tail sheath and the mitochondrial coat.

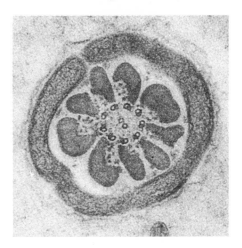

Fig. 3.10. Electron micrograph of cross section of rabbit sperm midpiece.

are considered to be the contractile units responsible for the movement of the tail, but it is not known why the rabbit spermatozoon (and other mammalian spermatozoa[1]) should require two rings of fibers, whether both these rings should be considered active in contraction, or what is the function of the two central fibers. The swimming movement of the spermatozoon takes the form of a wave or bending couple that originates at the base of the tail, possibly in the proximal and distal centrioles, and is propagated distally. Near the head, the bending couple is two-dimensional, but as it passes toward the distal end it becomes somewhat three-dimensional, imparting a helical twist which causes the spermatozoon to rotate about the axis of its forward progression.

Macrogametes, oöspheres, ova, eggs

Macrogametes vary much less obviously in structure than do microgametes, but here too details differ for each species, and even for strains within a species. The most clear-cut difference is probably that of size (Figs. 3.11–3.13). The size of macrogametes is chiefly attributable to the amount of stored nutrient material or yolk present; in addition, the eggs of reptiles, birds, and monotremes have a coating of albumen (egg "white") which subserves both nutritive and protective functions. Reptile eggs have very little white; those of snakes virtually none. Large, yolky eggs are characterized as megalecithal, while the smaller, relatively yolk-free eggs are called microlecithal. Embryos

[1] The outer ring of fibers is best developed in mammals, but its possession is not restricted to mammals; the 9 + 9 + 2 pattern is also known in the honeybee *Apis mellifera*, the snail *Helix pomatia*, the fruit fly *Drosophila melanogaster*, the grasshopper *Gelastorrhinus bicolor*, the sparrow *Passer montanus saturatus*, and the snake *Lampropeltis getulus*.

developing in megalecithal eggs are independent of environmental sources of food materials for prolonged periods of time; microlecithal eggs yield embryos that must obtain nutrient from the outside very early, either by becoming parasitic on the maternal organism (as in mammals, some teleost fish such as the cyprinodonts, elasmobranchs like the dogfish *Mustelus*, some amphibia such as the Surinam toad *Pipa dorsigera*, and some coelenterates such as *Hydra*), or rapidly achieving an active food-seeking larval stage (as in insects, tunicates, and many marine invertebrates). In the higher plants, embryos depend upon nutrient materials deposited, not in the oösphere, but in tissues surrounding the early embryo (the endosperm) or in modified leaves (cotyledons). Eggs may be "naked," having no membranes or investments other than the plasma membrane (as in the sporozoans, bryophytes, and pteridophytes), or they may have one or more proteinaceous

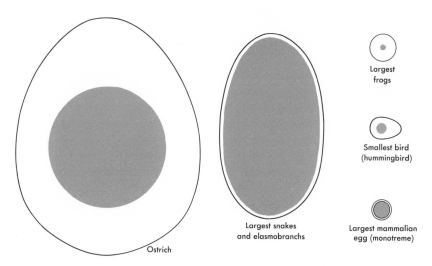

Largest
frogs

Smallest bird
(hummingbird)

Largest snakes
and elasmobranchs

Largest mammalian
egg (monotreme)

Ostrich

Fig. 3.11. Over-all sizes of eggs, with yolks gray.

or mucoproteinaceous membranes or coverings (many marine invertebrates, some amphibians, some fish, marsupials, and placental mammals), chitinous external cases (insects, elasmobranchs), calcarious shells (tortoises, birds), or keratinous envelopes (most other oviparous reptiles, monotremes).

Eggs of sea urchin and rabbit

The eggs of the sea urchin and rabbit consist of a spherical cytoplasmic body, the vitellus, which has a diameter of 72 μ in the sea

Fig. 3.12. Outlines showing sizes of egg vitel-
luses. Large circle represents the monotreme egg.
Some of the largest invertebrate eggs are those
of the squid *Loligo*, the gastropod *Busycon*, the
starfish *Henricia*, and the crab *Libinia*. The largest
marsupial egg, that of the Australian native cat
Dasyurus, is about the same size as the egg of
the sea-squirt *Amaroucium*. The sizes of most
mammalian eggs correspond to those of many
echinoderms, tunicates, molluscs, polychaetes,
nemertines, platyhelminths, and coelenterates.
The smallest mammalian egg, that of the field
vole *Microtus agrestis*, corresponds in size to the
egg of the clam *Spisula*. The smallest animal eggs
include those of the bryozoan *Crisia* and the
mesozoan *Dicyema*. Redrawn from C. R. Austin,
The Mammalian Egg (Blackwell Scientific Publications, 1961).

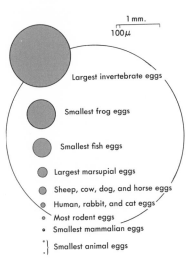

Largest invertebrate eggs

Smallest frog eggs

Smallest fish eggs

Largest marsupial eggs

Sheep, cow, dog, and horse eggs

Human, rabbit, and cat eggs

Most rodent eggs

Smallest mammalian eggs

Smallest animal eggs

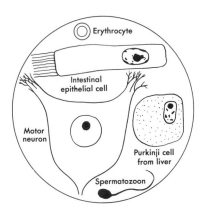

Erythrocyte

Intestinal
epithelial cell

Motor
neuron

Purkinji cell
from liver

Spermatozoon

Fig. 3.13. Relative sizes of some
mammalian cells. The enclosing outline represents the circumference of
the vitellus of the smallest mammalian
egg (that of the field vole).

urchin and 110 μ in the rabbit. The vitellus contains many granules and
droplets of various sizes representing the yolk or deutoplasm, and, in
addition to the usual cell organelles, certain specialized elements known
as cortical granules, which are disposed immediately under the surface.
The cytoplasm of the sea-urchin egg is limited by the so-called vitelline
membrane, 150 to 200 Å thick, which appears to consist in fact of two
unit membranes in close apposition. Each cortical granule is enclosed
by a single unit membrane which is a diverticulum of the inner layer
of the compound vitelline membrane (Fig. 6.5). After sperm penetration,

the layers separate, the outer one becoming, with additions of cortical granule material, the fertilization membrane, the inner being recognized as the plasma membrane (see "Exclusion of surplus spermatozoa" in Chapter 6). The plasma membrane of the rabbit egg is evidently a simple unit membrane and is not known to change in thickness after sperm penetration.

Both sea-urchin and rabbit eggs complete their growth in the ovary as primary oöcytes, characterized by the possession of a large spherical nucleus (the germinal vesicle—similar to that of the rat egg, Figs. 1.1 and 1.4) which generally has a single large nucleolus. The nucleolus contains RNA and is surrounded by an irregular aggregate of chromatin. The sea-urchin egg is shed from the ovary at this stage and then undergoes maturation, which is normally completed before sperm penetration occurs (Table 5.1); by contrast, the rabbit egg begins to mature before leaving the ovary and is ovulated when the second maturation division is in metaphase.

The sea-urchin egg (like that of *Echinarachnius*—Fig. 3.14) is invested with a wide (50 to 100 μ) clear jelly coat, composed chiefly of a mucopolysaccharide known as fertilizin. The rabbit egg displays a transparent membrane 12 to 15 μ thick, the zona pellucida, which is mucoprotein in composition and corresponds to the thick "vitelline membrane" of certain invertebrate eggs, such as those of *Mytilus* and *Hydroides;* it is separated from the vitellus by a narrow, fluid-filled perivitelline space (Fig. 3.15). When first ovulated, the rabbit egg is surrounded in addition by a close-packed array of follicle cells and a mass of jellylike material in which many more follicle cells are embedded; this is the cumulus oöphorus. The jellylike matrix is a hyaluronic acid–protein complex. The cumulus normally disintegrates during fertilization, and the rabbit egg, passing now along the Fallopian tube, becomes covered by yet another investment, the mucin coat, which achieves a thickness of 50 to 100 μ. Mucin-coat deposition occurs only in the Lagomorpha among placental mammals, but is also seen in the marsupials (Fig. 3.15).

Gametogenesis in animals

The origin of the gametes is demonstrable in organisms in which there is a difference in the chromosome number in the cells of germ and soma lines. Thus, in the roundworm *Parascaris equorum*, the four cells formed by the second cleavage division, identified by the letters A, B, C, and P, show differences in nuclear behavior. In Cells A, B, and C, but not in P, a large part of each chromosome passes into the cytoplasm and breaks up ("chromatin diminution"). At the next division, one of the daughter cells of P shows chromatin diminution, but not the other, and the same sort of thing happens at the fourth division,

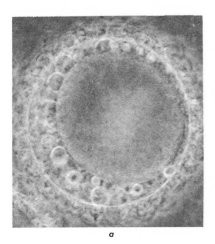
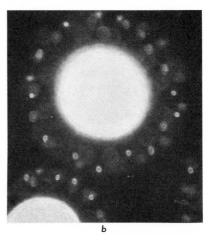

a   b

Fig. 3.14. Two marine eggs. (a) The ascidian *Ciona*. Surrounding the vitellus at a short distance is the chorion, on the inside of which appear the test cells, and on the outside the follicle cells. (b) The sand dollar *Echinarachnius*. Pigment granules embedded in the jelly coat permit the thickness of this layer to be appreciated.

so that only one cell, P_4, retains the full chromosome number. It is from P_4 that all the germ cells eventually develop, their identification depending on their possession of undiminished chromatin. Various lines of evidence have made it clear that the factor ultimately responsible for cells becoming germ cells resides in the cytoplasm, and it is known as the germ-cell determinant. In many eggs, this has been shown to occupy the basophilic yolk-free cytoplasm at the vegetal pole. Any competent nucleus passing into the area of the germ-cell determinant is capable of becoming the nucleus of a germ cell. Often the determinant appears to include deeply staining granules that are present in the vegetal cytoplasm and that become aggregated at one pole of the first four cleavage spindles (Fig. 3.16). The single blastomere that then contains the granules is the source of all the germ cells. Such granules have been described in the eggs of scyphozoans, chaetognaths, rotifers, insects, crustaceans, and amphibians.

The primordial germ cells arising during cleavage continue to multiply during embryonic development and enjoy a curiously independent existence. In all forms studied, the primordial germ cells occupy extragonadal regions until the gonadal rudiments are fairly well differentiated, whereupon they migrate into the developing gonads and take up initially a cortical location.

In mammals, the primordial germ cells are first recognizable in the posterior yolk-sac endoderm; from here they move through the tissues

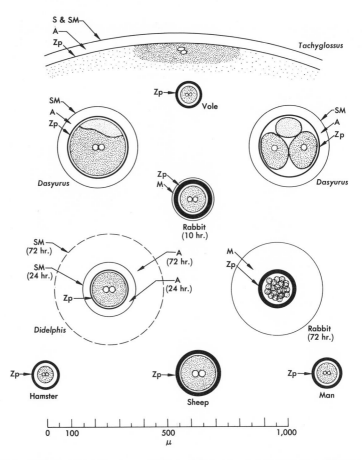

Fig. 3.15. Various mammalian eggs, showing relative sizes and identity of membranes and investments. Developmental stages shown are pronuclear syngamy for each animal and, in addition, a stage of cleavage for the Australian native cat *Dasyurus* and the rabbit. Accretion of the albumin coat (A) by the egg of the opossum *Didelphis* and of the mucin coat (M) by the rabbit is indicated by the inclusion of outlines for two periods after ovulation (24 and 72 hours for *Didelphis*, and 10 and 72 hours for the rabbit). Notable is the much greater thickness of the zona pellucida (Zp) in the placental mammals. S = shell. SM = shell membrane. Redrawn from C. R. Austin and E. C. Amoroso, *Endeavour*, 18 (1959), 138.

until they reach the genital ridges. As the gonads differentiate, the primordial germ cells give rise to spermatogonia and oögonia in testis and ovary, respectively. After further multiplication, gonial cells form primary spermatocytes and primary oöcytes. These undergo the first meiotic division to give secondary spermatocytes and oöcytes, and then the second meiotic division to give spermatids and oötids—a succession of events referred to as the maturation of the germ cells. Without further cell division, spermatids differentiate into spermatozoa. As a result of meiosis, four spermatids are formed from one primary spermatocyte, and one oötid and three polar bodies from one primary oöcyte. Owing to the occurrence of crossing over, all the products of meiosis tend to differ in genetic constitution, and it is probable therefore that few if any spermatids or oötids produced by individual animals are genetically identical. In practice, three polar bodies are rarely seen: the first polar body generally fails to divide and often breaks up and disappears before ovulation.

The differentiation of a spermatid into a spermatozoon (spermateleosis) involves a series of changes that are remarkably similar through a wide range of metazoan forms; these are illustrated diagrammatically in Fig. 3.17. Within the Golgi apparatus, small vesicles

Fig. 3.16. Origin of the germ cells in the copepod *Cyclops*. The cytoplasmic germ-cell determinant, e, becomes segregated during cleavage so that it occupies only one cell in the morula (g). From this cell arise the primordial germ cells of the organism. Redrawn from K. Amma, *Ztschr. Zellforsch.*, 6 (1911).

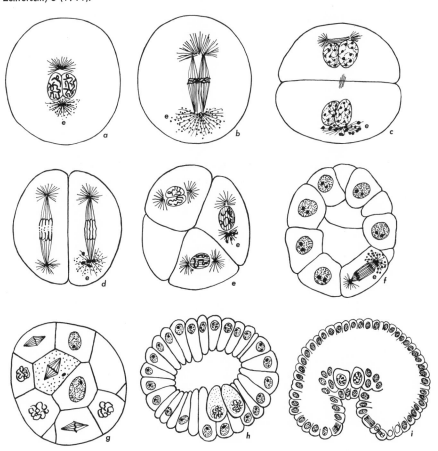

develop, each containing a homogeneous granule. These enlarge and coalesce so that a single vesicle with granule results (the "acrosome vesicle" and "acrosome granule") and becomes attached to the surface of the nucleus. In different animals, the acrosome vesicle and granule may remain projecting from the nucleus (and later from the front surface of the sperm head) or to varying degrees become spread out over the surface of the nucleus, as the nucleus moves to the periphery of the cell. As development proceeds, the acrosome vesicle appears to contract so as to become wholly occupied by granule substance. During the early stages of acrosome formation, the two centrioles move to the plasma membrane of the spermatid and one of them, probably the "mother" centriole and destined to be the distal centriole of the spermatozoon, becomes attached to the membrane. From the point of attachment a fine thread, resembling a cilium, grows out; this is the primordium of the axial filament of the future tail. The centrioles then return to a position close to the nucleus and at the opposite pole to that occupied by the early acrosome. The tail filament is thus drawn apparently into the cytoplasm, but the plasma membrane is carried inward also and forms a double sheath about the filament, so that the filament is still in fact outside the cell. Later, the ring centriole, developing from distal centriole, carries the membrane fold back to the general cell surface. Mitochondria become associated with the axial filament, in the wake of the ring centriole, to form the midpiece, and the outer ring of nine coarse fibers grows down from the proximal centriole to bulk out the tail. Meanwhile, the nucleus of the spermatid has emerged from the cytoplasm and soon assumes a shape similar to that of the mature sperm head. In the terminal stages of spermateleosis, the cytoplasmic cell body is discarded, except for a small residue, the cytoplasmic droplet, which remains until the spermatozoon has traversed the epididymis.

Gametogenesis in plants

In some thallophytes, as in the brown alga *Fucus*, the plant is diploid, and the haploid gametes are derived through two meiotic divisions in much the same way as in most animals. In other members of the phylum, however, such as in the common green alga *Oedogonium*, the plant is haploid, gamete formation is mitotic, and meiosis takes place after fertilization in the initial stages of spore formation (Fig. 5.6). Thus, though the homologues of primary spermatocytes and oöcytes occur in *Oedogonium*, there are no homologues of secondary spermatocytes and oöcytes or of spermatids and oötids. This is the state of affairs also in bryophytes, where a sporophyte generation is introduced between fertilization and spore formation. Similarly, in the higher

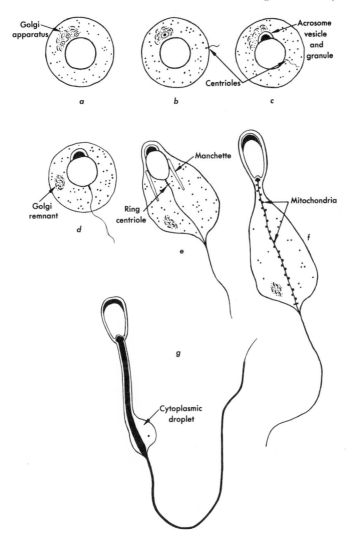

Fig. 3.17. Spermateleosis in the rabbit. (a) Small vesicles appear within the Golgi apparatus, each containing a granule. (b–c) Vesicles and granules coalesce, and the single structure thus formed becomes apposed to the nuclear surface as the acrosome vesicle and granule. At the same time, the fine tail filament develops from the two centrioles when they lie adjacent to the plasma membrane and then follows the centrioles to the nucleus, accompanied by its membrane sheath. (d) The "spent" Golgi apparatus moves away from the nucleus as the Golgi remnant and the acrosome vesicle and granule undergo further enlargement and become spread out on the nuclear surface. The tail filament protrudes from the cytoplasm. (e–f) The nucleus emerges from the main cytoplasmic body (a movement in which the manchette may play some role), and the ring centriole appears and moves down the tail, while mitochondria become disposed on the tail in its wake. (g) The nucleus assumes the form characteristic of the mature spermatozoon and most of the cytoplasmic body is shed, leaving a small droplet that is retained while the spermatozoon passes into the epididymis.

plants, meiosis occurs in the diploid sporophyte during the formation of the haploid microspore (pollen grain) and megaspore (embryo sac), which give rise to haploid gametes by mitosis.

Spermateleosis in plants has some resemblance to the process in animals, but details differ. Since the male gamete of a plant is not required to make its way through specialized egg membranes, homologues of acrosomal elements are lacking. The most striking feature lies in the development of the ciliated band that characterizes the spermatozoids of most ferns and the cycads (Fig. 3.3). In the spermatid, the centrioles multiply until a large number are formed, and these become arranged in a long row; from each there arises a cilium so that a spiral band of cilia is produced. As in animals, a residuum of cytoplasm is retained for a while after the general structure of the mature spermatozoid has been formed, and finally this is shed.

FOUR

Approximation of Gametes

The meeting of conjugants in populations of unicellular organisms is no doubt promoted by the same mobility that is important in the search for food materials, but among such creatures the frequency of meetings is determined very largely by chance. The probability of encounter is increased with the production by both simple and complex organisms of large numbers of specialized gametes. This is especially evident among aquatic organisms exhibiting external fertilization; to offset the effects of dilution by the surrounding medium, and of wastage due to predators or adventitious losses, the output of gametes often achieves prodigious proportions, and the animals become virtually gamete factories in the breeding season, with most of the body cavity occupied by gonads. Clearly, reproductive patterns of this kind involve enormous losses, and a much higher efficiency is attained when the pattern includes special devices that facilitate encounter between gametes. Preoccupation with germ-cell production diminishes throughout living organisms as the effectiveness of these auxiliary mechanisms increases. The series culminates with the angiosperms, in which each male and female gametophyte yields, respectively, only two microgametes and one megagamete.

Special devices facilitating gamete encounter are of many kinds, but can be grouped into three categories: (1) elaboration of chemical agents capable of attracting or trapping male gametes, (2) mechanical juxtaposition of gametes, and (3) synchronization in the production and release of gametes. Most reproductive patterns involve processes belonging to at least one of these categories, and in many a high level of efficiency

51

is attained, but always there remains in addition some element of chance in the meeting of gametes.

Chemical attraction or trapping of male gametes

Chemical attraction of the male gamete (involving movement classifiable as a chemotaxis) is of acknowledged occurrence only in the bryophytes and pteridophytes. In these plants, the oösphere is held at the base of the flask-shaped archegonium, the neck canal of which is filled with mucilage. Some of the mucilage oozes from the open end of the canal, and chemical components are released into the surrounding water. Spermatozoids suspended in the water are attracted from a distance, gather near the entrance, and make their way up the canal to the oösphere. Careful observations on several members of these two groups make it clear that the spermatozoids react to the presence of the chemical agents by changing their direction of swimming so that they pass into regions of increasingly higher concentrations of the agent. The nature of the attracting substance varies: apparently a protein in the liverwort *Pellia*, sucrose in the moss *Funaria*, and L-malic acid in the bracken fern *Pteridium*.

Numerous claims have been made that a chemotactic response of spermatozoa is demonstrable in animals; but in no instance has the possibility been properly excluded that the apparent attraction was in reality attributable to the existence of conditions limiting the escape of spermatozoa that strayed by chance into the vicinity of the eggs. Aggregation of gametes under these conditions need not imply the existence of any kind of attraction, but is evidence rather of a trapping effect. There is a fundamental difference between these two mechanisms: to show a chemotactic response, the spermatozoon must be able to distinguish between small differences in concentration of a chemical substance over a wide range of concentrations; for a trapping action, it is sufficient that the spermatozoon react to a concentration above a certain threshold. Mechanisms involving chemotaxis are no doubt the more efficient, but the value of a trapping action cannot be much less and is greatly improved by prolificacy of gamete production. In addition, it has often been noted that when spermatozoa enter a trapping zone their motility is augmented, an effect that may further increase the probability of gamete encounter.

In animals, the possibility that chemotaxis is operative seems most likely in coelenterates and in fish. Thus, in *Campanularia*, spermatozoa released into the sea water must find the opening of a female gonangium and make their way down to the eggs within—circumstances reminiscent of those surrounding sperm entry into archegonia of primitive plants. Spermatozoa gather about the entrance to the gonangium in increasing numbers, though they are not often seen to orientate their movements toward the gonangium from a distance, and some are successful in swimming away again. Spermatozoa near the gonangium opening show increased motility. Isolated pieces of tissue removed from around the gonangium entrance (but not from any other part of the hydranth) also produce aggregations in suspensions of spermatozoa. Similar phenomena are seen in fish, such as the medaka, bitterling, fat-minnow, salmon, trout, and sturgeon. Spermatozoa in the surrounding medium may show little motility, but when they come close to the surface of the chorion they exhibit vigorous swimming movements. They evince also a strong tendency to gather about the micropyles (minute openings in the chorion that provide the only access to the vitellus). Small pieces of chorion bearing a micropyle produce the same effects, whereas the vitelline surface exposed by removal of the chorion is without influence; the active agent evidently emanates from chorion lining the micropylar canal (Fig. 5.5). The consequence is that spermatozoa approaching an egg seem to be encouraged to find and enter a micropyle, and here they can readily come into contact with the small tongue of egg cytoplasm that extends into the canal (see "Sperm entry by way of micropyles" in Chapter 5).

A trapping effect can also be regarded as involved in the more or less specific attachment that occurs between gametes in a wide range of species (see Chapter 5). The cumulus oöphorus that persists about the eggs of many mammals at the time of sperm penetration may serve to retain in the vicinity of the eggs spermatozoa that would otherwise have passed by.

Mechanical juxtaposition of gametes

In mammals, a number of mechanical agencies are involved in bringing together eggs and spermatozoa. At coitus, the spermatozoa are propelled along the vas deferens and urethra by muscular action in the walls of these organs and are projected into the female genital tract (into the vagina of the rabbit, dog, cat, ewe, cow, and human being; into the cervix of the horse; and into the uterus of the pig and the rodent). From their point of deposition in the female tract, spermatozoa are transported through the uterus and Fallopian tube, again mainly by muscular activity of the walls of the organs, into the ampulla of the tube. On release from the ovary, the egg is carried into the ampulla by fluid movement, attributed to the beating of cilia lining the mucous surface of the infundibulum and ampulla. It is in the ampulla, in most species, that the gametes meet and fertilization begins; evidently only in the final approach of spermatozoon to egg does sperm motility play a role in this process (except, it seems, in the rabbit where the slow transit of the uterus is commonly attributed to dependence of sperm transport on motility). Thus mechanical agencies in the female tract are mainly responsible for the efficient transport of spermatozoa, but it is important to note that these agencies do not work only toward this goal—spermatozoa passing along the tract are subject to progressive reduction in number through dilution in the mucous secretions, dissemination over the extensive mucous surfaces, and obstruction by the barriers provided by the abrupt constrictions of the tract, such as occur at the cervix and the uterine ostium of the Fallopian tube (the uterotubal junction). Transport of spermatozoa is thus a compromise between efficient conduction and restriction in number—between almost certain assurance of fertilization and avoidance of such numbers of spermatozoa at the site of fertilization as would promote the occurrence of polyspermy (the nature and consequences of which are considered in Chapter 7). As a result, the number of spermatozoa that has been found at the site of fertilization is remarkably small—less than 100 in the rat, mouse, and hamster, about 200 in the field vole, and less than a thousand in the rabbit, dog, and sheep (Fig. 4.1). It is conceivable that mechanisms reducing sperm numbers would also have the effect of selecting for the more vigorous or the more compatible spermatozoa; that such a mechanism is possible is shown by the evidence that mouse spermatozoa carrying a certain gene

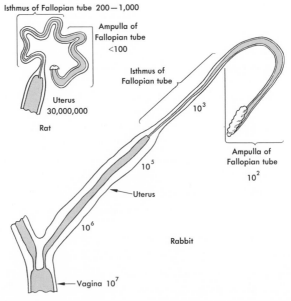

Fig. 4.1. Changes in lumen diameter in the genital tracts of the rat and the rabbit, and the numbers of spermatozoa reaching different regions. Ejaculation in the rat is into the uterus, and in the rabbit into the vagina.

(the *t* allele) tend to be selectively prevented from entering the Fallopian tube and reaching the site of fertilization.

Mechanical factors of a similar kind may well operate to varying degrees in nonmammals when coitus is the means of transferring spermatozoa between individuals, but other mechanisms certainly exist too. Coition, with introitus, is employed in reptiles, some amphibians (coecilians and the "tailed" frog *Ascaphus truei*), some teleosts (e.g., the ciprinodonts), elasmobranchs, most insects, some annelids (e.g., oligochaetes such as the earthworm), some gastropods (e.g., snails, and the slipper limpet *Crepidula*), and the turbellarians, trematodes, and cestodes. Spermatozoa are deposited in specialized recipient cavities in most instances, but in acoeles, and some rhabdocoeles and polyclads, hypodermic insemination occurs—the penis of the male is armed with stylets that puncture the body wall of the female and permit spermatozoa to be introduced directly into the mesenchyme. In many species, spermatozoa are stored in a special receptacle in the female called a spermatheca, where they can be held in a dormant state for prolonged periods (for months or even years in certain reptiles and insects). Storage for several months in the female genital tract, though not in spermathecae, is known also in some mammals—namely, in the bats *Myotis* and *Eptesicus*. Coition, without introitus, is seen in birds, the semen being ejaculated from the genital papilla of the male into the cloaca of the female. In anurans (frogs and toads) and in the horseshoe or king crab *Limulus*, the male grasps the female from the back, and eggs and spermatozoa are shed into the surrounding water in close proximity; this form of sexual act is known as amplexus.

Many other devices are employed in the bringing together of eggs and spermatozoa. In spiders and crustaceans, a forward limb or palp is modified for the function of taking up the semen (directly from the male duct or after deposition on a special "sperm web") and introducing it into the genital opening of the female during the courtship ritual (Fig. 4.2). In the cephalopods, one of the arms is modified for the function of holding spermatophores and is referred to as the hectocotylus. During courtship, the male seizes a bundle of spermatophores as they emerge from the male duct with his hectocotylus arm and places them either in the mantle cavity or in the seminal receptacle of the female. On contact with sea water, the spermatophores undergo a sudden "ejaculatory reaction," and each releases a simple sac packed with spermatozoa but open at one end (Fig. 4.3). The sac adheres to the wall of the mantle cavity or the seminal receptacle, and the spermatozoa escape over a period of many hours, becoming vigorously motile with suspension in sea water. Eggs are usually laid within a few hours of mating and are penetrated by spermatozoa as they pass through the mantle cavity or while held in the arms just before being attached to the substratum.

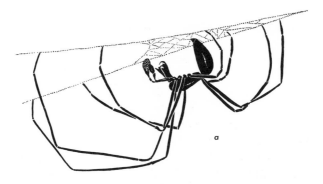

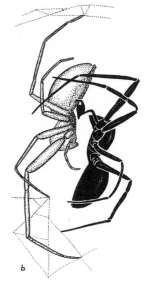

Fig. 4.2. Mating in spiders; examples from two different species which adopt the same procedures. In (a), the male is shown on the sperm web, filling his palps from a droplet of semen. In (b), the palps are being used to introduce the semen into the copulatory openings of the female. Redrawn from R. D. Barnes, *Invertebrate Zoology* (Saunders, 1963).

In American and Australian varieties of peripatus, spermatophores are deposited in the female cloaca, but in the African variety (*Peripatopsis*), they are applied to almost any part of the body surface. Spermatozoa leave the spermatophores, penetrating the body wall in the case of *Peripatopsis*, and make their way through the tissues until they reach the ovary, where fertilization takes place (Fig. 4.4). Conditions found in *Peripatopsis* are seen also in the bug *Cimex* and the leech *Clepsine*. In urodeles (salamanders), the spermatozoa are incorporated in the tip of a conical spermatophore which, initially plastic, becomes firm soon after deposition (Fig. 4.5). During the courtship "dance," the male deposits the spermatophore on the ground, and the female, moving over, takes it up with the lips of her cloaca. Scorpions, too, have a courtship dance, and the male attaches a rodlike spermatophore to the rock or other surface

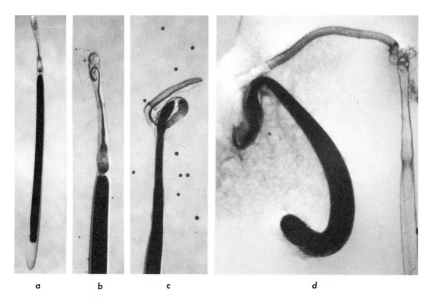

a   b   c   d

Fig. 4.3.   The spermatophore of *Loligo pealii*. (a) The intact spermatophore; (b) the ejaculatory apparatus. (c) and (d) are two stages in the reaction of the spermatophore, which involves a complete eversion of the ejaculatory apparatus. The extruded sperm sac can be seen in (d), spermatozoa in large numbers escaping from the open end.

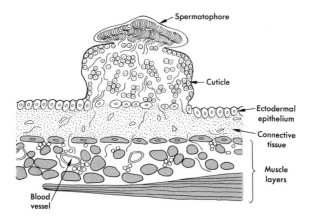

Fig. 4.4.   The spermatophore of *Peripatopsis*. A form of blister arises where the spermatophore is attached, and here the cuticle breaks down, allowing spermatozoa to reach the deeper tissues. Redrawn from S. M. Manton, *Phil. Trans. Roy. Soc. (London)*, Ser. B., **228** (1938), 421.

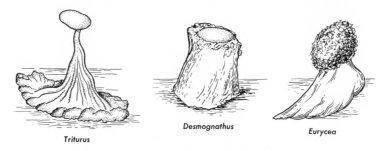

Desmognathus

Eurycea

Triturus

Fig. 4.5.   Salamander spermatophores.

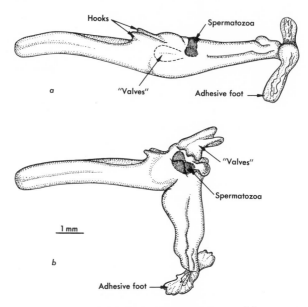

Fig. 4.6.   Spermatophore of the scorpion *Opisthophthalmus latimanus*. (a) As deposited by the male on the substratum, the spermatophore lies more or less horizontally, anchored by the adhesive foot. During the courtship "dance" the operculum of the female scorpion engages the hooks. (b) As a result, the spermatophore "snaps," the lower part becomes erect, and the spermatozoa are projected into the female's genital pore, guided by the "valves." Redrawn from A. J. Alexander, *African Wild Life, 16* (1962), 313.

beneath him. He then maneuvers the female over the spot until the operculum of her genital pore strikes a pair of hooks on the spermatophore; contact causes the spermatophore to "snap" in the middle, and the spermatozoa, which lie encased at that point, are projected into the genital pore (Fig. 4.6).

Spermatophores have also been described in some crustaceans (copepods, euphorsiaceans), mites, pseudoscorpions, in chætognaths, and even in fish (Fig. 4.7). In many other animals, spermatozoa are emitted in

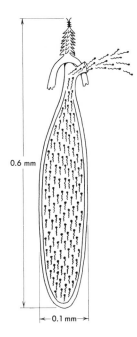

Fig. 4.7. Spermatophore of the teleost *Horaichthys*. The male sheds close to the female; the semen is a suspension of large numbers of spermatophores, and many of these become attached to the female near or on the genital orifice. Spermatozoa escaping from the spermatophore swim into the female tract, or meet eggs as they emerge.

0.6 mm

0.1 mm

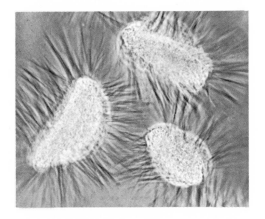

Fig. 4.8. Sperm packets (spermatozeugmata) as shed by *Pectinaria*. After a few minutes in sea water, the spermatozoa become motile, disaggregate themselves, and swim away.

small packets or spermatozeugmata, wherein the cells are held together by some form of mutual attraction and no enveloping sheath or capsule is present (Fig. 4.8).

Mechanical transport could also be said to occur in the spermatophytes, for the male nuclei, originating in germinating spores or pollen grains, are carried in pollen tubes and released in the close vicinity of the oösphere (Fig. 4.9). Then again, in sponges, the spermatozoon does not enter the egg directly but enters one of the surrounding choanocytes, and this cell establishes cytoplasmic continuity with the oöcyte (evidently through fusion between its plasma membrane and that of the egg) and deposits the spermatozoon in the egg cytoplasm (Fig. 4.10).

Synchrony in production and release of gametes

Many mammals exhibit a clear-cut periodicity of sexual activity, the pairing of sexes and participation in coitus occurring only during a limited period of each year. This period is the breeding season, and its

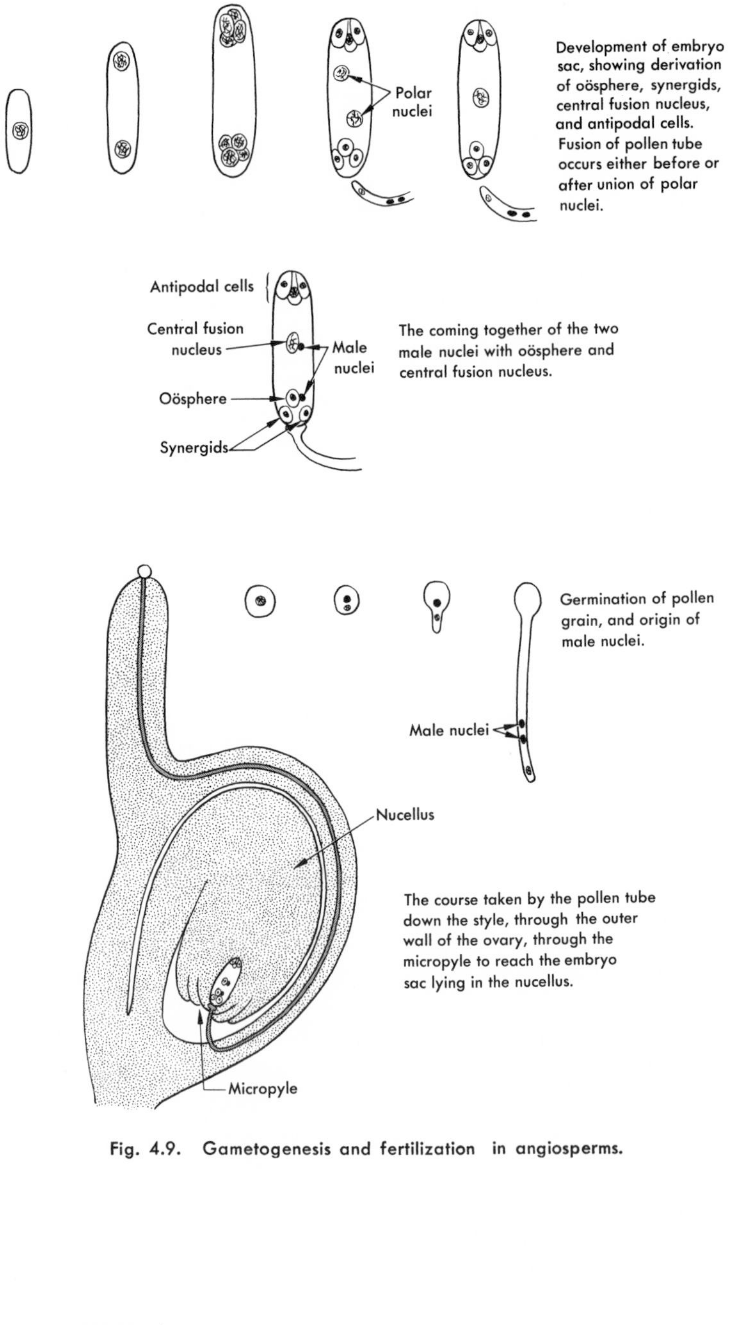

Development of embryo sac, showing derivation of oösphere, synergids, central fusion nucleus, and antipodal cells. Fusion of pollen tube occurs either before or after union of polar nuclei.

Polar nuclei

Antipodal cells

Central fusion nucleus

Male nuclei

Oösphere

Synergids

The coming together of the two male nuclei with oösphere and central fusion nucleus.

Germination of pollen grain, and origin of male nuclei.

Male nuclei

Nucellus

The course taken by the pollen tube down the style, through the outer wall of the ovary, through the micropyle to reach the embryo sac lying in the nucellus.

Micropyle

Fig. 4.9.   Gametogenesis and fertilization   in angiosperms.

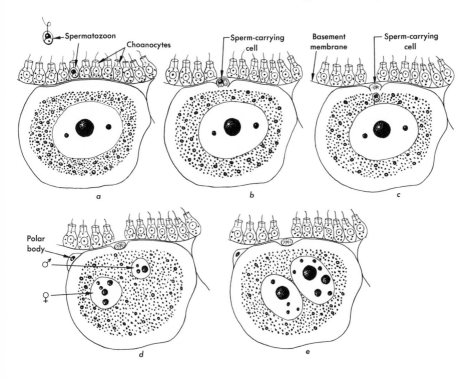

Fig. 4.10. Fertilization in the sponge *Grantia compressa*. The spermatozoon consists of nucleus and mitochondrion (dark), enclosed in a small body of cytoplasm, and a tail. (*a*) It enters a choanocyte or collar cell, which becomes transformed into a sperm-carrying cell; the two now pass through the basement membrane of the choanocyte epithelium and come into contact with the oöcyte surface. (*b*) Cytoplasmic continuity is then established between the sperm-carrying cell and the oöcyte, and (*c*) the spermatozoon moves into the egg cytoplasm. (*d*) Meiosis takes place, with the formation of two polar bodies (of which one is shown), and male and female pronuclei develop (♂, ♀). (*e*) Stage of full pronuclear development. Redrawn from J. B. Gatenby, *J. Lin. Soc., Zool.*, 34 (1920), 26.

onset and termination are determined by changes in day length: in autumn breeders, such as the sheep, a diminishing day length induces an increased pituitary hormone output that initiates the breeding season, while in spring breeders like the horse the stimulus is an increasing day length. Spermatogenesis and ovulation in many mammals, particularly the wild creatures, are restricted essentially to breeding seasons, the testes and ovaries returning to a quiescent state for the remainder of the year. Within the breeding season, it is common to find that the male is continuously sexually receptive and that the female's receptivity is cyclic: she will take part in coitus only when in the comparatively short-lived condition of "heat," or oestrus, which recurs at definite intervals of time. The periodic and usually regular return of oestrus distinguishes the oestrous cycle, and some animals, such as the horse, cow, sheep, goat, pig, and the rodents, show a succession of oestrous cycles. Other animals, like the dog, do not have a succession of cycles, but experience a single oestrous period every six months; here, breeding season and oestrous period are synonymous. In the cat, oestrus is exhibited four or five times during the breeding season, which occupies about eight months of the year (Table 4.1).

It is only during oestrus, and usually late in that phase, that ovulation occurs (a rare exception being the cow, in which ovulation takes place 10 to 15 hours after the end of oestrus), and the restriction of sexual receptivity has the obvious advantages of conserving effort and ensuring the best prospects for the meeting of fully viable eggs and spermatozoa. Even greater economy of eggs is achieved in animals that have induced ovulation; the term is applied to ovulation that is not spontaneous but occurs only in consequence of coitus—erotic stimuli give rise to nerve impulses that provoke the release from the anterior hypophysis of gonadotrophic hormones, and these in turn act on ovarian follicles, causing them to ripen, rupture, and release the eggs. Induced ovulation is found in a variety of mammals, including the rabbit, hare, mink, ferret, lynx, cat, raccoon, common shrew, ground squirrel, field mouse, and field vole. These animals exhibit oestrus several times during their breeding season, and on each occasion they remain in oestrus for several days or even weeks, or until they participate in coitus (Table 4.1).

In a sense, induced ovulation has a counterpart in many nonmammalian animals with external fertilization, in which the shedding of gametes (of both kinds) is stimulated by the close proximity of individuals of the opposite sex or by the presence of the corresponding gametes (as in oysters, sea urchins, and nereids, which have been studied extensively).

Some nonmammals are also strongly influenced in their breeding activity by daylight—notably the birds. In several species, it has been shown experimentally that growth and maturation of the gonads can be induced by artificially increasing day length, and conversely that gonad regression can be induced by decreasing day length. Some lizards and turtles also respond in this manner. Among the marine invertebrates there are a number in which the shedding of the gametes is closely associated with the onset of light or dark. Thus, in the coelenterates *Gonionemus* and *Eutima* shedding occurs soon after dark, while in *Hydractinia* and the tunicate *Molgula* it occurs in the first hour or so of daylight. In the coelenterate *Pennaria* and the tunicate *Styela*, gametes are shed after ten to fourteen hours of light.

Thus far, attention has been given only to the effects of daylight, but in certain animals it is moonlight that is important. Some bats, birds of crepuscular habit such as the nightjar, fish such as the Canadian smelt and the New Zealand whitebait, and some marine polychaete worms give

Table 4.1. Time relations of oestrus and ovulation.

Animal	Oestrous periods					Ovulation	
	Breeding season	No. in season	Length (range or mean)	Intervals between	Induced or spontaneous	Hours after coitus	Relation to oestrus
Rat	All year*	Many	10–20 h.	5 d.	S	About 10	10 h. from start
Mouse	All year*	Many	10–20 h.	4–5 d.	S	Varies	2–3 h. from start
Golden hamster	All year*	Many	12 h.	4 d.	S	Varies	6 h. from start
Guinea pig	All year*	Many	6–12 h.	15 d.	S	Varies	10 h. from start
Squirrel (Citellus tridecemlineatus)	Spring	Several	—	—	I	8–12	10 h. from start
Field mouse (Microtus pennsylvanicus)	Most of the year	Many	—	—	I	15	—
Shrew (Blarina brevecorda)	Spring and summer	—	Prolonged	—	I	55–71	—
Rabbit	Spring and summer	1‡	Prolonged	—	I	10	—
Ferret	Spring and summer	1‡	Prolonged	—	I	30–90	—
Mink	Spring	Several	2 d.	Varies	I	36–50	—
Cat	Except winter	4–5‡	7–10 d.	14 d.‡	I	24–54	—
Dog	Twice in year	1	9 d.	6 m.	S	Varies	1–2 d. from start
Ewe	Autumn and winter*	Many	27 h.	16 d.	S	Varies	Near end
Cow	All year*	Many	18 h.	20 d.	S	Varies	≯ 20 h. after end
Sow	All year*	Many	50 h.	21 d.	S	Varies	35 h. from start
Mare	Spring and summer	Many	7 d.	23 d.	S	Varies	1–2 d. before end
Woman	—	—	28 d.†	—	S	Varies	14 d. before menstruation

* Under domestication.
† Menstrual period.
‡ In absence of coitus.

h. = hours
d. = days
m. = months

evidence of depending upon phases of the moon for coordination of their sexual activities. Especially striking is the palolo worm *Eunice viridis*, which normally lies hidden among rocks on the sea floor but rises to the surface waters and spawns in prodigious numbers at dawn of the day before and the day on which the moon enters its third quarter in the months of October and November.

Generally speaking, however, cold-blooded animals are much more sensitive to temperature changes than to changes in illumination. The level of bodily activity of poikilothermic animals, like their body temperature, closely follows the rise and fall of environmental temperature, and it is consistent that gonadal function in various frogs, fish, and coelenterates has been found to be controlled by temperature changes and to be unaffected by light.

Other environmental factors also affect breeding seasons, and probably the most important is nutrition, which is capable of influencing sexual activity in all organisms. It is likely that the cyclic reproductive phases in many insects are dependent upon corresponding changes in the vegetable life that provides their food; in turn, the reproductive patterns of plants are largely fashioned by variations in light intensity, temperature, and rainfall. Clearly, the coordination of sexual activity that serves to raise the probability of gamete encounter is, in most living organisms, subject primarily or ultimately to control by climate.

FIVE

Contact and Fusion of Gametes

Among isogamous unicellular organisms, conjugation involves attachment (or agglutination) and cytoplasmic fusion, although fusion in the bacteria and ciliates is temporary, and its extent is sufficient merely to permit chromosomal transfer or nuclear exchange, respectively. Union of heterogamous gametes also proceeds by attachment and fusion, but, especially in more complex organisms, may be complicated by the presence of specialized membranes and investments about the macrogamete. Sometimes there is an opening in these coverings; more often they must be pierced by the microgamete. Where this is necessary, it has been shown in many animals to depend upon the occurrence of an acrosome reaction which involves release of a lytic agent and the forward projection of one or more acrosome filaments. Actual sperm-egg union then begins with fusion of sperm filament membrane with egg plasmamembrane. Cytoplasmic fusion is followed by approximation and union of specialized gamete nuclei (pronuclei), one or both of which may develop only after the start of cytoplasmic fusion. Nuclear union usually involves the gathering of egg and sperm chromosomes into a single group; this is the culminating point of fertilization, the immediately succeeding steps (division and separation of chromosomes) representing the start of the first cleavage division of the zygote. In angiosperms, two male nuclei are involved at each fertilization, one combining with the oösphere nucleus and the other with the two polar nuclei or their product, the central fusion nucleus.

Initial attachment

The attachment that occurs between individual paramecia was mentioned in Chapter 3 in connection with mating types. It is, in the first instance, nonspecific, and if the individuals are not of complementary mating types, they soon separate. Where they are complementary, attachment is prolonged; to begin with, it is in the "holdfast" region near the anterior pole of each cell, and later by means of paroral cones that develop from each cell (Fig. 5.22). Finally, fusion occurs over part of the contact area between paroral cones (see "Cytoplasmic fusion" later in this chapter).

Among the Metazoa, attachment between spermatozoa and eggs has been studied most extensively in marine invertebrates, the classic work being especially on sea-urchin gametes. In these, it was first demonstrated that sea water in which eggs have been allowed to stand in the laboratory (egg water) has the capacity to agglutinate spermatozoa. The reaction turned out to be attributable to the substance of the jelly coat (fertilizin) which goes slowly into solution; fertilizin is a glycoprotein with a molecular weight of 82,000 or more. Agglutination of spermatozoa by homologous egg water has been demonstrated in members of several groups, including the echinoderms, annelids, molluscs, tunicates, and vertebrates. It was shown in the sea urchin to be caused by reaction between fertilizin and a substance on (and extractable from) the surface of the spermatozoon; the sperm substance was named antifertilizin and has been identified as an acidic protein. The fertilizin-antifertilizin reaction is moderately species specific, and for this and other reasons it has been likened to a reaction between antigen and antibody. The analogy helps to explain the reversibility of agglutination of sea-urchin spermatozoa and the inability of the disagglutinated spermatozoa to become reagglutinated. It is postulated that fertilizin in solution is multivalent, the molecules being capable of linking together several spermatozoa; disagglutination and failure of reagglutination are ascribed to splitting of the fertilizin molecule, the parts of which, now in the form of univalent fertilizin, remain attached to the receptor sites on the sperm surface and thus block further reaction. Disagglutinated spermatozoa are also incapable of fertilization. These observations are interpreted to mean that the normal function of fertilizin lies in the attachment of homologous spermatozoa to the jelly-coat surface, and that this is a necessary preliminary to fertilization. There is evidence, however, that fertilizin is also a component of the plasma membrane of the egg. Since fertilization can occur in eggs deprived of their jelly coat, or that normally lack a jelly coat, it is considered that reaction between antifertilizin of the sperm plasma-membrane and fertilizin of the egg plasma-membrane may constitute the essential feature of specific attachment of the gametes. Fertilizin and antifertilizin would represent then the receptor substances of egg and spermatozoon respectively, and the relative species specificity of the reaction would tend to prevent entry of foreign spermatozoa.

Agglutination of spermatozoa by egg water has also been demonstrated with mammalian gametes, the source of the active agent being apparently the zona pellucida, and here too there is said to be a measure of species specificity. Attachment of homologous spermatozoa to the zona surface would no doubt promote penetration of that membrane, but the zona pellucida is separated from the vitellus by the perivitelline space, and so the fertilizing spermatozoon must also form an attachment at the egg plasma-membrane. This second attachment is fairly protracted (it has been estimated to last about half an hour in the rat, mouse, and hamster), and, since it involves a direct association between plasma membranes, it is analogous to paroral attachment in *Paramecium*.

The relative species specificity of attachment between gametes is probably the main factor underlying the specificity of fertilization, though the selective action of many egg-membrane lysins probably also bears a measure of responsibility. It is generally accepted that specificity of gamete attachment can be ascribed to complementariness in the molecular patterns of proteins or mucoproteins on their contact surfaces, and these substances should have distinctive antigenic properties. Accordingly, attempts have often been made to prepare appropriate antisera capable of agglutinating or affecting the fertilizing capacity of spermatozoa. In sea urchins, it has in fact been possible to show, by sperm agglutination tests, that the *Arbacia* sperm surface has at least three antigens or antigenic complexes. One of these is found also on *Lytechinus* spermatozoa, and another on both *Lytechinus* and *Echinarachnius* spermatozoa; a third is not shared with either of these genera. Anti-*Arbacia* sperm antisera, rendered nonagglutinating (univalent) by papain digestion, are capable of inhibiting fertilization, but the mechanism involved remains to be elucidated. In mammals the antigens commonly detected on ejaculated spermatozoa are primarily those found in the seminal plasma, but species-specific surface antigens may also be demonstrated, particularly in epididymal spermatozoa. Also, it is possible to induce the formation of autoantibodies against spermatozoa, and there are indications, both from research and clinical experience, that a reaction to spermatozoa may be built up in the female to such a degree that sterility supervenes through inhibition of fertilization.

Sperm entry by way of micropyles

The presence of small holes or micropyles in the membranes surrounding eggs has been described in some nemertines, gastropods, pelecypods, and echinoderms, and seems to be a universal feature in insects (Fig. 5.1), cephalopods (Fig. 5.2), and fish, excluding lampreys (Fig. 5.3). In eggs of the first group, the micropyle is normally single and probably represents no more than the site at which the egg was originally attached to the ovary; spermatozoa can enter these eggs through other parts of the surface and appear to pass through the micropyle merely adventitiously. In insects and fish, there are often several micropyles, and in these animals and cephalopods the micropyle provides the only portal for sperm entry.

The lamprey egg is surrounded by a resistant membrane or chorion and bears a "tuft" of jellylike material at the animal pole (Fig. 5.4). Around the tuft there is a narrow region of naked chorion, and the remaining two-thirds of the surface is invested with a thick layer of jelly. Though there is no evidence for the existence of micropyles in these eggs, it has been observed that the penetration of spermatozoa is restricted to the area covered by the relatively small tuft at the animal pole.

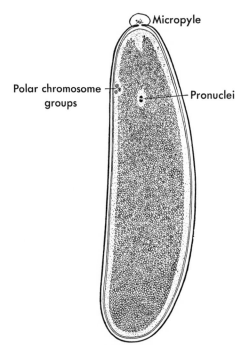

Fig. 5.1. The egg of the fly *Musca*. A small jellylike mass exudes from micropyle. The pronuclei are uniting.

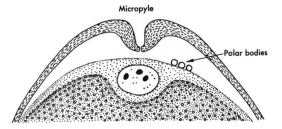

Fig. 5.2. The egg of the cephalopod *Argonauta*. The micropyle lies in a deep pit. Redrawn from M. Ussow, *Arch. Biol.*, 2 (1881).

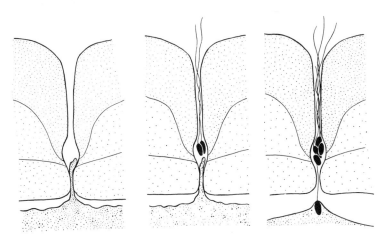

Fig. 5.3. Entry of spermatozoa into the egg of the sturgeon. The micropyle traverses the three layers of chorion, and into its lower reaches projects a tongue of vitelline cytoplasm. Contact with and attachment to the cytoplasm appears to be necessary for the spermatozoon to complete its journey through the micropyle. Redrawn from A. S. Ginsburg, *Cytologia, 1* (1959), 510.

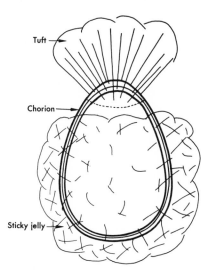

Fig. 5.4. The egg of the lamprey *Lampetra*. Sperm entry occurs only through the "tuft" at one pole. Redrawn from R. A. Kille, *Exp. Cell Res.*, 20 (1960), 12.

The chorion of insect, fish, and cephalopod eggs is thick and tough. In many insects, the chorion is deposited in the ovary; as the egg passes the spermatheca after leaving the ovary, spermatozoa have access to it and enter by means of the micropyles. In the cephalopods, the relationships are similar: the egg is shed complete with chorion, first into the mantle cavity and thence to the exterior; at shedding, spermatozoa enter the eggs through the micropyles. The eggs in most groups of fish are fertilized after shedding and quite outside the body; the male releases large numbers of spermatozoa over the egg clutch, and these must find their way to the eggs and into the micropyles. Sperm motility is provoked or greatly increased when they get close to the surface of the chorion and seems to aid in their finding the micropyles (Fig. 5.5).

Apertures bearing the name of micropyle are also found in spermatophytes and in algae such as *Oedogonium* (Fig. 5.6). In the former the term denotes the space between the lips of the nucellar investments through which the tip of the pollen tube carrying the microgametes may pass (porogamy) or not (chalazogamy). In *Oedogonium* it denotes the slit or pore in the oögonial wall that admits the spermatozoid to the egg.

Egg-membrane lysins

Studies on sperm penetration have been made on several forms since the entry of the spermatozoon into the egg was first described in *Ascaris* and the frog, and the idea that penetration is made possible by the solvent action of sperm enzymes upon egg investments has achieved a wide acceptance. Some years ago, it was shown that the thin but resistant membrane enclosing the egg of the keyhole limpet *Megathura crenulata* was readily dissolved by sperm extracts. The lytic agent was proved to be enzymic by the demonstration that it was nondialyzable, thermolabile, and gave protein reactions. Spermatozoa of several different sea urchins have yielded membrane lysins active on the jelly coat as well as on the vitelline membrane, and lysins have been obtained from spermatozoa of the mussel *Mytilus edulis*, the abalone *Haliotus* spp., and the polychaete worms *Pomatoceros triqueter* and *Hydroides hexagonus* (Fig. 5.18) that are active on the vitelline membranes (0.5 to 5 μ thick) of these animals. Inferences concerning the function of artificially extracted lytic agents should, however, be drawn with caution, for it is possible that some may be autolytic enzymes not normally brought to bear on egg membranes during the course of sperm penetration. In the sea urchin, there is evidence that the spermatozoa can make their way into the jelly coat and reach the

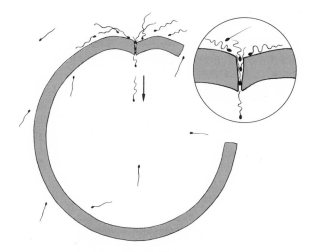

Fig. 5.5. Behavior of spermatozoa near the chorion of the herring (*Clupea*) egg, after removal of the vitellus. The spermatozoa are motionless until they drift onto the surface of the chorion near the micropyle. They then show vigorous motility and soon swim into and through the micropyle. Redrawn from R. Yanagimachi, *Anat. Zool. Japan*, 30 (1957), 114.

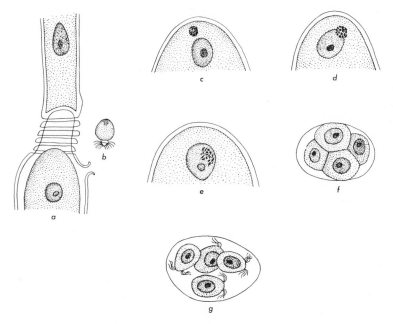

Fig. 5.6. Fertilization in the alga *Oedogonium*. The egg lies in an oögonium (a) that can be entered by the spermatozoid (b) through the micropyle. A small, colorless patch of egg cytoplasm immediately below the micropyle is the "receptive spot;" from it exudes a mucinous material that attracts the spermatozoids. (c–e) Union of male and female pronuclei. (f) and (g) The zygote becomes divided into four zoospores through two meiotic divisions.

vitelline membrane without the aid of jelly-splitting enzymes, so that the presence of such agents in sperm extracts is probably an artifact. At the same time, there is little doubt that the spermatozoa of many species do rely on lytic agents at some stage of entry, and in *H. hexagonus* and *M. edulis*, for example, spermatozoa leave distinct holes in the vitelline membrane after they have passed through (Fig. 5.18). Another aspect of the problem is that true membrane lysins may not always be extractable in an active form, their activity depending possibly upon specific orientation at the surface of the sperm head.

The presence of the lytic agent hyaluronidase in mammalian semen has long been recognized, as has its capacity to liquefy the matrix of the cumulus oöphorus surrounding ovulated eggs. The enzyme is derived from the spermatogenic epithelium and is not found in the secretions of the accessory organs. Thus, it is clearly associated with the spermatozoon (almost certainly with the acrosome) and not with the seminal plasma, but the plasma comes to contain hyaluronidase as spermatozoa die and release their quanta of enzyme. The concentration of hyaluronidase in the semen is higher in some mammals (e.g., the bull) than others (e.g., the dog); traces have also been reported in fowl and snake semen.

Observations increasingly indicate that living mammalian spermatozoa are unable to release hyaluronidase until they have undergone some form of physiological change, which normally occurs in the female genital tract and to which the name *capacitation* has been given. In consequence of this change, the acrosome is modified (see "Acrosome reaction," below), and hyaluronidase is released. The eggs of some animals (horse, cow, sheep) lose their cumulus investment shortly after ovulation, so that spermatozoa can gain direct access to the zona pellucida. In most other animals, however, the cumulus persists for several hours and presents a barrier that can only be penetrated by spermatozoa that are releasing hyaluronidase.

The evidence for capacitation of spermatozoa in the female genital tract is mainly circumstantial and depends on the demonstration in rabbits and rats that fertilization did not begin as soon as eggs and spermatozoa came into the same vicinity but only after the spermatozoa had spent some hours in the tract (see Fig. 5.7). Until 1963, experience with fertilization of mammalian eggs in vitro (see Chapter 7) had been consistent with the idea, for success had been achieved only with rabbit eggs treated with uterine spermatozoa recovered several hours after coitus. Observations with the hamster reported in that year, however, indicate that capacitation can take place under appropriate conditions in vitro.

In those animals in which the cumulus oöphorus breaks up soon after ovulation, capacitation may still be required for sperm penetration, for there are indications that acrosome change must precede passage through the zona pellucida also. The spermatozoon apparently makes its way through this membrane too with the aid of an enzyme, and narrow curved slits made by penetrating spermatozoa can be seen in the zona pellucida of pig, rabbit, rat, mouse, guinea pig, and Libyan jird eggs.

The need for capacitation or an analogous process may well exist in nonmammals also. In the frog, for example, uterine eggs (which have a jelly coat) are readily fertilized under experimental conditions, while

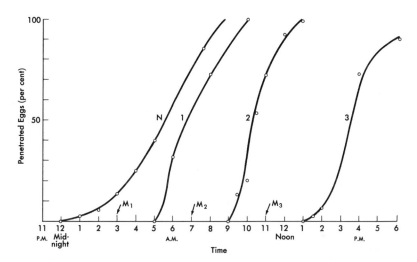

Fig. 5.7. Proportion of penetrated eggs found in rats at various times after coitus. N = Normal mating (which generally occurred late the previous afternoon). 1, 2, and 3 = Coitus at 3 A.M., 7 A.M., and 11 A.M., respectively (M_1, M_2, M_3). With this delayed mating, no penetrated eggs were found earlier than $2\frac{1}{2}$ hours after coitus, but thereafter the proportion increased rapidly. Since spermatozoa reach the site of fertilization in well under half an hour, the delay of sperm penetration into eggs is ascribed to a need for the prior capacitation of the spermatozoa in the female tract.

body-cavity eggs (lacking the jelly coat) are resistant. If jelly coats removed from uterine eggs are placed around body-cavity eggs, however, fertilization can be effected. Fertilization even of the naked body-cavity eggs takes place if the spermatozoa are first suspended in egg water from uterine eggs.

Lysins can, of course, be inhibited by appropriate enzyme inhibitors, and various compounds have been tested against hyaluronidase with the ultimate objective of controlling human fertility. The most active have been Rehibin, a gentisic acid–formaldehyde polymer, and a substance identified as 53D/k, which is a hydroquinone sulphonic acid–formaldehyde polymer. Both agents inhibit hyaluronidase in vitro in concentrations that have little or no effect on the motility of spermatozoa, and both can prevent fertilization when applied to sperm suspensions prior to artificial insemination. Neither, however, has been effective in preventing fertilization when tested in rabbits by systemic administration to the doe. Compound 53D/k is also capable of preventing fertilization of sea-urchin eggs; the spermatozoa pass through the jelly coat in the normal way but fail to pierce the vitelline membrane. The action, both in mammal and sea urchin, may not be attributable only to lysin inhibition; the compound has a strong affinity for cell surfaces, and there is some evidence with the sea-urchin material that the acrosome reaction is prevented.

Acrosome reaction

The spermatozoa of the river lamprey and several marine invertebrates, notably certain bivalve molluscs, sea urchins, starfish, and holothurians, and the enteropneust *Saccoglossus*, have been found to react to contact with jelly coat or egg membrane by projecting a filament, the acrosome filament, in a forward direction from the head and generally toward the vitellus (Fig. 5.8). In many instances, filament formation can be provoked by treating the spermatozoa with egg water. It is regularly accompanied by alteration in the shape of the acrosome, and the composite change is termed the acrosome reaction; there is often also a simultaneous shift in the position of the midpiece. The filament is relatively short and thick in some forms, and long and thin in others. In the sea urchin, the spermatozoon makes its way through the jelly coat with intact acrosome, and the acrosome reaction appears to be evoked by approach to or contact with the vitelline membrane; the short, thick filament characteristic of these animals is adequate then to reach the cytoplasm. The *Nereis* spermatozoon, too, has a short, thick filament; this filament is preformed but becomes expanded in the acrosome reaction. In the starfish, the holothurians, and *Saccoglossus*, on the other hand, the spermatozoon seems incapable of advancing directly into the jelly coat; the acrosome reaction occurs with the sperm head in contact with the jelly surface, and a remarkably long, thin filament is produced which reaches the egg cytoplasm. The acrosome filament of the lamprey spermatozoon is also a long, fine structure. It is logical to infer that the lytic agents released when the acrosome reacts (see "Egg-membrane lysins," above) make possible the passage of the sperm head through the investment pierced by the filament.

A detailed electron microscopic study has been made on the gametes of the polychaete worm *Hydroides hexagonus*, in which the acrosome

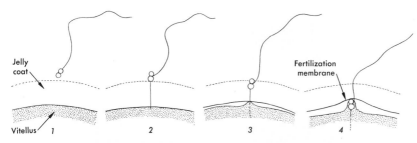

Fig. 5.8a.   Acrosome reaction in *Asterias*. (1) Approach of spermatozoon. (2) Acrosome reaction provoked by contact with jelly coat surface, and projection of filament into vitelline surface. (3 and 4) Absorption of spermatozoon, and formation of fertilization cone and membrane.

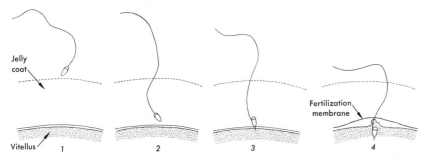

Fig. 5.8b.   Acrosome reaction in *Arbacia*. (1) Approach of spermatozoon. (2) Passage of spermatozoon through the jelly coat. (3) Acrosome reaction provoked by contact with vitelline membrane, and projection of filament into vitelline surface. (4) Absorption of spermatozoon, and formation of fertilization cone and membrane.

reaction is hardly distinguishable by light microscopy. From this study, it is evident that contact with the vitelline membrane induces first a fusion between the plasma membrane covering the acrosome and the immediately subjacent acrosome membrane (Fig. 5.9). As a result, the acrosome opens and the lytic agent is released to act upon the substance of the vitelline membrane. As penetration proceeds, the conjoined plasma-acrosome membrane shrinks back toward the nucleus, and small elevations of the inner layer of the acrosome membrane in the region overlying the nucleus increase rapidly in length so as to form distinct fingerlike processes or tubules. Finally, these processes reach the vitelline surface and become accommodated in deep invaginations of the egg plasma membrane (Fig. 5.18).

Electron microscopic observations of a less complete nature have been made in several sea urchins and in *Asterias*, *Nereis*, and *Saccoglossus*. In these spermatozoa, the acrosome reaction results in the production of a single filament instead of a number of processes, but basically the course of the reaction seems to be the same as in *Hydroides:* fusion of

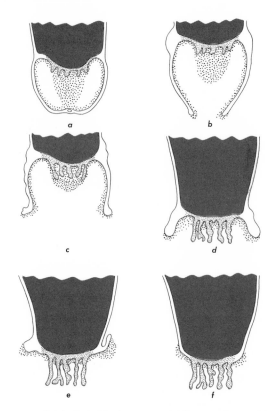

Fig. 5.9.   Acrosome reaction in *Hydroides hexagonus*. (a) Intact acrosome. (b) On contact with vitelline membrane, fusion occurs between the plasma membrane and the outer acrosome membrane. The lytic agent in the acrosome is thus released. (c–f) As the sperm head moves through the vitelline membrane, the sides of the acrosome subside onto the nucleus and the fingerlike projections of the inner acrosome membrane increase in length and complexity. Redrawn from L. H. Colwin and A. L. Colwin, *J. Biophysic. Biochem. Cytol.*, 10:2 (June, 1961), 231–54, by permission of the Rockefeller Institute Press.

plasma membrane and outer layer of acrosome membrane, release of lytic agent through the opening thus formed, and protrusion of inner layer of acrosome membrane so that it becomes the first part of the spermatozoon to come into close relationship with the egg plasma membrane (Figs. 5.10 and 5.11).

The indications are that a form of acrosome reaction occurs also in mammalian spermatozoa, and the mechanism could be of the same general character as in the marine animals just considered. In the rabbit and some rodents (golden hamster, Chinese hamster, guinea pig, Libyan jird) the acrosome, or a large portion of it, is lacking from spermatozoa that have penetrated the zona pellucida (Fig. 5.12). In the domestic pig, golden hamster, and guinea pig, spermatozoa recovered from the

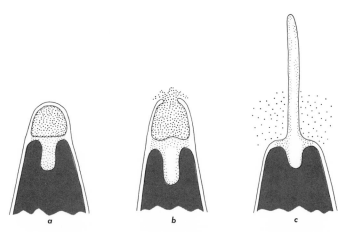

Fig. 5.10. Details of the acrosome reaction in *Arbacia*. (a) Intact acrosome. (b) Opening of the acrosome by fusion between the plasma membrane and the outer acrosome membrane; release of lytic agent. (c) Projection of the filament and reduction in bulk of material accommodated in the invagination of the anterior extremity of the nucleus.

Fallopian tube shortly after the time of ovulation exhibit modifications of the acrosome that can be discerned with the phase-contrast microscope. The changes take the form of a wrinkling or apparent elevation of the acrosome, together with a loss of visual contrast, and later there is a partial or even complete detachment of a membranous structure; these appearances can be seen in spermatozoa that are still actively motile (Fig. 5.13). A reasonable inference is that the changes are analogous to those of the invertebrate acrosome reaction: fusion of

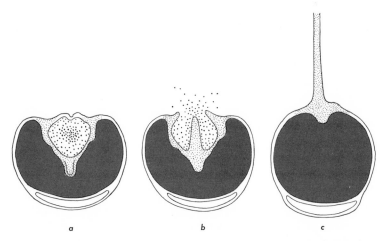

Fig. 5.11. Details of the acrosome reaction in *Asterias*. (a) Intact acrosome. (b and c) Opening of the acrosome by fusion between the plasma membrane and the outer acrosome membrane; release of the lytic agent; projection of the filament; big reduction in the size of the nuclear invagination. Interpretation of electron micrographs published by J. C. Dan, *Exp. Cell Res.*, *19* (1960), 13.

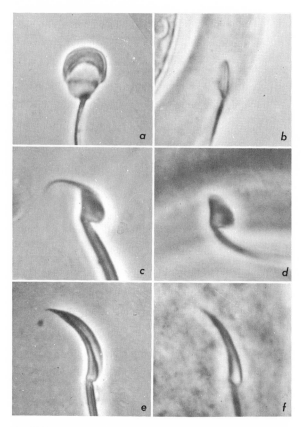

Fig. 5.12.   Acrosome loss in rodent spermatozoa. Heads of living spermatozoa. (a, c, and e) Epididymal spermatozoa of guinea pig, Libyan jird, and Chinese hamster, respectively. (b) Sperm head embedded in the zona pellucida. (d) Sperm head in the perivitelline space. (f) Sperm head lying on the surface of the vitellus, in an early stage of its absorption by the vitellus.

plasma membrane with outer acrosome membrane, opening of acrosome cavity, and release of lytic agent (here hyaluronidase). Observations on rabbit spermatozoa by electron microscopy support this idea (Fig. 5.14).

Cytoplasmic fusion

The next event in fertilization, after close approach by gametes or conjugants has been achieved, is cytoplasmic fusion. With certain conjugants, such as those in *Paramecium*, it has long been appreciated that, for nuclear transfer to occur, the cytoplasm of the two cells probably becomes continuous, even if only momentarily. On the other hand, until the end of the 1950's sperm entry into eggs was commonly held

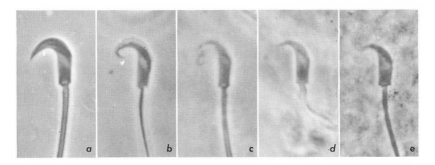

Fig. 5.13. Acrosome loss in the golden hamster. Heads of living spermatozoa. (a) Epididymal spermatozoon. (b) Spermatozoon recovered from the Fallopian tube. (c) Spermatozoon found among the cumulus cells. (d) Sperm head in the thickness of the zona pellucida. (e) Sperm head lying on the surface of the vitellus, in an early stage of its absorption by the vitellus.

to involve phagocytic engulfment of the spermatozoon by the vitellus. It is now known that, at least in some organisms and probably in all, both entry of spermatozoa and union of conjugants entail cell-membrane (plasma-membrane) fusion as the essential step in the establishment of cytoplasmic continuity. Fusion generally occurs in the region of first contact, and by this act the two cells become enclosed within the same membrane continuum and therefore constitute a single cell, though in the initial stages they appear still to retain their individuality. Detailed electron microscopic studies have been made on comparatively few species: the ciliate *Paramecium caudatum,* the alga *Prasiola stipitata,* the polychaete worm *Hydroides hexagonus,* the enteropneust *Saccoglossus kowalevskii,* and the laboratory rat. The cytoplasmic bridge demonstrable by electron microscopy between members of a mating

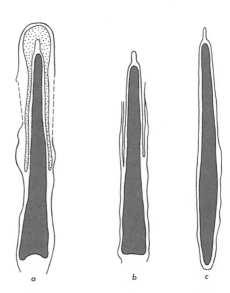

Fig. 5.14. Drawings made from electron micrographs of sections of rabbit spermatozoa found in the zona pellucida or perivitelline space of eggs. (Light stipple = acrosome; dark gray area = nucleus.) The broken lines in (a) indicate continuity of the plasma membrane which became disrupted in the preparation. Appearances presented by the three profiles are consistent with the idea that the acrosome reaction in the rabbit spermatozoon could well follow the same course of events as in the acrosome reactions of certain marine invertebrates (Figs. 5.9 to 5.11).

pair of bacteria (see "Nuclear union," below) may represent the region of fusion through which the chromosome passes at fertilization, but this is not yet known for certain.

Paramecium caudatum.   The surface structure of *Paramecium* is quite complex. The cilia and trichocysts are arranged in regular alternating rows; shallow vesicles, lying immediately beneath the cell membrane, occupy the regions between these bodies. In conjugation, as the cell membranes covering the paroral cones of the two participants become closely approximated, fusion occurs between points on the inner and outer walls of the vesicles, and then also between the cell membranes of the conjugants in regions exactly overlying these points (Figs. 5.15 and 5.16). In this way, a number of narrow channels of cytoplasmic continuity are established between the conjugants, providing passages for the transfer of the migratory nuclei.

Prasiola stipitata.   When effective contact occurs between the macrogamete and the tip of one of the two flagella of the microgamete, the cells become firmly attached so that continued movements of the

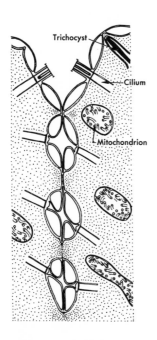

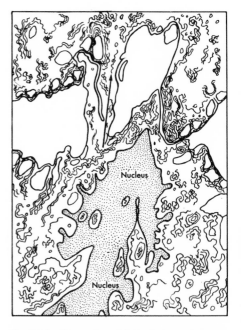

Fig. 5.15. The region of fusion between two paramecia. Redrawn from E. Vivier and J. André, *J. Protozool.*, 8 (1961), 416.

Fig. 5.16. The region of fusion between two paramecia. The arrow indicates a path of cytoplasmic continuity between the two organisms. Drawn from electron micrograph of J. André and E. Vivier, *J. Ultrastr. Res.*, 6 (1962), 390.

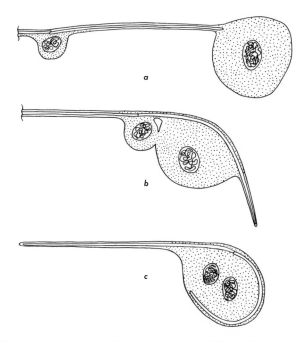

Fig. 5.17. Fusion of gametes in the alga *Prasiola stipitata*. (a) Soon after contact between the macrogamete and the tip of one flagellum of the microgamete (illustrated in Fig. 3.3), fusion occurs between their plasma membranes so that a single compound cell is formed. (b) Secondary fusion occurs when the cell bodies of the two gametes come in contact. (c) One flagellum still protrudes, but will eventually be drawn into the conjugate cell mass. Interpretation of electron micrographs of I. Manton and I. Friedmann, *Nova Hedwigia, 1* (1959), 443.

flagellum fail to separate them (Fig. 5.17). Fusion of plasma membranes originates at the region of attachment, and, as it extends, the core of the flagellum is drawn into the cytoplasm of the macrogamete. Then the cell body of the microgamete makes contact with the macrogamete and membrane fusion occurs here also, for at this stage of conjugation a circumscribed aperture can often be seen between the gametes. Eventually, the whole microgamete becomes engulfed, the second flagellum remaining for a while the only protruding part. The membrane limiting the zygote is considered to be a mosaic structure composed of the plasma membranes of the two gametes.

Hydroides hexagonus. The spermatozoon reaches the vitellus with the inner acrosome membrane, which covers the leading surface of the nucleus, thrown up into several fingerlike processes (see "Acrosome reaction," above, and Fig. 5.18). These processes become accommodated in invaginations of the egg plasma membrane, and it is in this region of interdigitations that fusion between the two membranes begins, evidently at several points simultaneously. In some places, the fusion

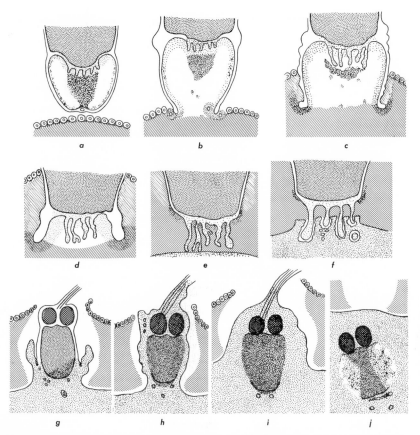

Fig. 5.18. Cytoplasmic fusion in *Hydroides hexagonus*. (a–c) Stages in the acrosome reaction, described in Fig. 5.9. (d) Accommodation of projections of the acrosome membrane in invaginations of the vitelline surface, which is soon followed by fusion between this membrane of the spermatozoon and the plasma membrane of the egg. (e and f) Passage of the sperm head into the vitellus. The egg cytoplasm flows up under the sperm plasma membrane and around the sperm head, midpiece, and tail, forming the fertilization cone. Note the perforation made by the solvent action of the sperm lysin on the vitelline membrane. Redrawn from L. H. Colwin and A. L. Colwin, *J. Biophysic. Biochem. Cytol.*, 10:2 (June, 1961) 255–74, by permission of The Rockefeller Institute Press.

process results in the detachment of small areas of egg and sperm membranes, so that small vesicles lined by two membranes are often seen. Egg cytoplasm now passes up around the sperm head, under the sperm cell membrane, and soon the midpiece and tail become surrounded. This elevation of egg cytoplasm represents the classic "fertilization cone." The complicated pattern of membranes produced by the initial interdigitation is soon lost, and, as the sperm nucleus, midpiece, and tail pass fully into the egg cytoplasm, the continuum of sperm-egg membranes comes to form an even contour to the zygote.

Saccoglossus kowalevskii. Cytoplasmic union in this organism involves essentially the same mechanisms as those in *H. hexagonus*, though details differ. In *S. kowalevskii*, a fine, long filament is produced as a result of the acrosome reaction, its covering being the former inner acrosome membrane. The filament traverses the two outer envelopes of the egg to reach the vitellus. Contact occurs between the tip of the filament and the vitelline surface, and in this area the membranes of the two gametes fuse. The gametes are now a single cell, though they appear to be connected only by a slender thread. Egg cytoplasm passes up under the sperm acrosome membrane and around the core of the filament, and eventually reaches the sperm nucleus, forming a taller and thinner fertilization cone than was evident in *H. hexagonus*. The cone subsides as the sperm nucleus, midpiece, and tail pass into the egg cytoplasm.

Laboratory rat. As yet, evidence for the occurrence of membrane fusion in mammals is based principally on sections of a single rat egg. The egg was in an early phase of fertilization, with the sperm head located just below the surface of the vitellus. The limiting membrane was clearly lacking from the sperm head, and the egg plasma membrane was continuous with the membrane covering the latter part of the midpiece and mainpiece of the tail that still projected from the egg cytoplasm (Fig. 5.19).

Cytoplasmic fusion naturally also raises questions relating to the role and fate of cytoplasmic elements in fertilization and embryonic development. With hologamous union, it is clear that the contributions of both gametes to the zygote are total, but problems arise when cytoplasmic fusion is partial and temporary, and when merogamy or heterogamy is involved. Nevertheless, it seems possible that some extranuclear transfer occurs in all organisms. In bacteria, there is known to be the transmission of the sex factor in $F^+ \times F^-$ crosses; in *Paramecium*, the passage of kappa particles between individuals of killer and sensitive clones; and in algae, such as *Cutleria-Aglaozonia* (Fig. 2.5), the contribution of plastids by the microgamete. In most metazoans, the sperm tail enters the vitellus at fertilization (exceptions are the polychaete worm *Nereis* and, among mammals, the field vole and the Chinese hamster), and in many invertebrates the sperm centriole serves as the

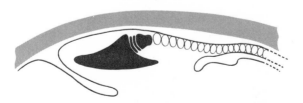

Fig. 5.19. Diagram based on electron micrographs shows a spermatozoon just below the surface of the vitellus in a rat egg. Through fusion, sperm and egg plasma membranes are now continuous, though only the sperm head and part of the midpiece lie as yet within the egg cytoplasm. Redrawn from D. G. Szollosi and H. Ris, *J. Biophysic. Biochem. Cytol.*, 10:2 (June, 1961), 275–83, by permission of The Rockefeller Institute Press.

kinetic center for the first cleavage division. (The mammalian first-cleavage spindle seems often to be independent of the sperm centriole—see "Polyandry" in Chapter 7.) Usually too, sperm mitochondria become dispersed in the egg cytoplasm, and can sometimes be followed as they are distributed between blastomeres in the cleavage stages of the embryo.

Nuclear union

With the establishment of cytoplasmic continuity between gametes or conjugants, the way is clear for the last phase in the process of fertilization—the union of nuclei. These nuclei are known as pronuclei; they are haploid in chromosome number (Fig. 5.20). In the essentially simple step of pronuclear union, there is a wealth of difference in detail in different organisms. In some instances, cytoplasmic fusion is very limited in extent and transitory in duration, and a chromosome or nucleus virtually unaccompanied by cytoplasm is passed from one cell to the other to take its place in the genetic apparatus of the recipient. More generally, complete fusion of gametes occurs, and is the principal mechanism for bringing the pronuclei together. Then again, differences are seen in the fact that at the time of cytoplasmic fusion, some pronuclei have already developed and possess the form they will have when they come into apposition, whereas others have yet to arise, from chromosome groups or specialized sperm nuclei. Finally, there are differences

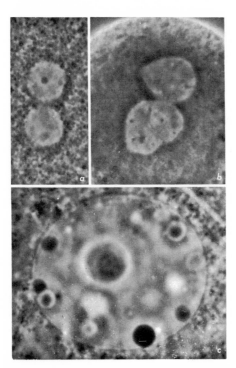

Fig. 5.20. Photographs of pronuclei in living eggs. (*a*) *Asterias*. (*b*) *Pectinaria*. (*c*) Rat. Magnification: 1,500 ✕.

in the degree of union achieved by the two pronuclei—in some organisms they merely approach closely, clearly retaining their individuality, while in others complete fusion, and presumably complete intermingling of chromosomes, takes place. Intermediate degrees of union are also known. Irrespective of these differences, pronuclear union remains a mechanism that ensures the gathering of maternal and paternal chromosomes in a single zygote, with the consequence that they become equally apportioned between the daughter cells at the first cleavage division, and diploidy is established in the embryo.

In bacteria, a single chromosome is passed from a donor (*Vhf*, *Hfr*, or "male") organism to a recipient (*F⁻*, or "female"), and there is some evidence from electron microscopy that this takes place through a cytoplasmic tube extending between the members of a mating pair. The chromosome to be transferred is evidently synthesized in the preliminary phase of pairing. The transfer is relatively slow, the whole process taking about an hour and a half. A mating pair may separate before transfer is complete, so that in any group of bacteria in which fertilization has occurred, there is a wide range of variation in the proportion of genetic determinants transferred. Variation is also seen in the fact that the bacterial chromosome seemingly exists in a circular form before transfer, and the break that must precede transfer can occur at almost any point in the circle. One of the "free ends" then precedes in the passage from donor to recipient. In the recipient bacterium, the new chromosome is incorporated into the genome, but the precise mechanism of recombination is not yet clear (Fig. 5.21).

In some fungi, such as *Basidiobolus* (Fig. 3.1), the extent of cytoplasmic fusion between conjugating mycelia is quite limited and little more than required for the passage of the "male" pronucleus into the "female" mycelium. A single zygote nucleus is formed. In other fungi, the male gamete penetrates the female cell with a cytoplasmic antheridial tube, but this is withdrawn after the male pronucleus has been released in close proximity to the female pronucleus. Nuclear fusion then ensues. Somewhat analogous processes take place in angiosperms, in which, however, the pollen tube penetrates, not the oösphere, but the embryo sac or a synergid, and one of the released sperm nuclei makes its way into the oösphere and fuses with the female pronucleus.

Ciliates are distinguished by having two kinds of nuclei—a large macronucleus that is responsible for metabolism and the genic control of the phenotype, and one or more small micronuclei that are the reproductive nuclei and also give rise to the macronucleus. The macronucleus plays no part in conjugation, but usually breaks up during or after the process. When cytoplasmic continuity is established at the paroral cone between two conjugating paramecia, each conjugant possesses two micronuclei (pronuclei) of haploid chromosome number which have been

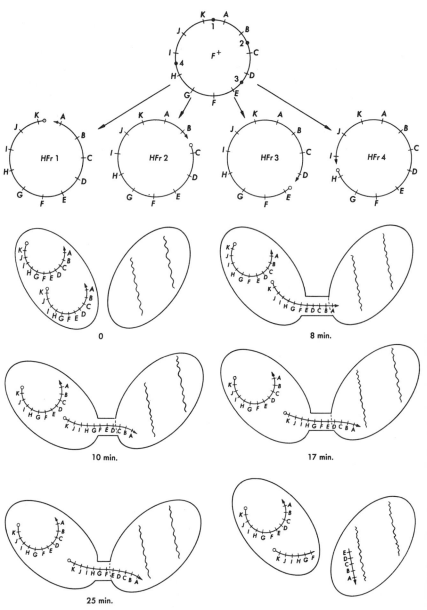

Fig. 5.21. Chromosome transfer in bacteria. The chromosomes of bacteria in the F^+ state seem to exist as complete circles, with the genes (A to K) disposed at various points. Genes on such chromosomes are not transferred. If the bacterium undergoes mutation to an Hfr type, the chromosome circle opens, the position at which it opens determining the lineal order of the genes (four possible results are shown—Hfr1, Hfr2, Hfr3, and Hfr4). The direction of transfer also varies, as indicated by the arrowheads at the ends of the chromosomes. The small circles denote the location of the sex factor. At conjugation, a chromosome is passed slowly from "male" to "female" bacterium; thus, in the case of the Hfr1 mutant, gene A is transferred in about 8 minutes, gene B in 9 minutes, gene C in 10 minutes, gene D in 17 minutes, gene E in 25 minutes, and so on. Conjugants may now become separated, so that no further genes can be transferred. In the recipient, the new chromosome becomes incorporated in the genome.

formed by meiotic divisions from original micronuclei. One, usually noticeably smaller, micronucleus is the "migratory nucleus," and the other the "stationary nucleus." Migratory nuclei are exchanged between the conjugants and become closely applied to the stationary nuclei, which have remained within their respective cells; nuclear fusion yields zygote nuclei. The two organisms separate and are now referred to as exconjugants; in each, the normal nuclear status is soon re-established, in the same cell or after one or more cytoplasmic divisions (Fig. 5.22).

Where total cell fusion of specialized gametes occurs, as in lower plants and most animals, certain nuclear changes may be required before the pronuclei come together. Generally, the nucleus in a spermatozoon displays a characteristic and compact state; in its transformation into

Table 5.1.   Stage of egg maturation at which sperm penetration occurs in different animals.

Young primary oöcyte	Fully grown primary oöcyte	First metaphase	Second metaphase	Female pronucleus
Brachycoelium	Ascaris	Aphryotrocha	Amphioxus	Coelenterates
Dinophilus	Dicyema	Cerebratulus	Most mammals	Echinoids
Histriobdella	Dog and fox	Chaetopterus	Siredon	
Otomesostoma	Grantia	Dentalium		
Peripatopsis	Myzostoma	Many insects		
Saccocirrus	Nereis	Pectinaria		
	Spisula			
	Thalassema			

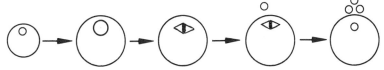

a male pronucleus, it often swells as though by a process of hydration and comes to assume more or less the form of an interphase nucleus (Fig. 5.23). The female pronucleus may already be formed at the time of gamete fusion, as in sea urchins and coelenterates, but otherwise the changes involved in the development of the pronucleus depend on the stage of meiosis in the female gamete (Table 5.1). In the extreme case, that of some annelids and platyhelminths, the spermatozoon enters the primary oöcyte early in its intra-ovarian existence and

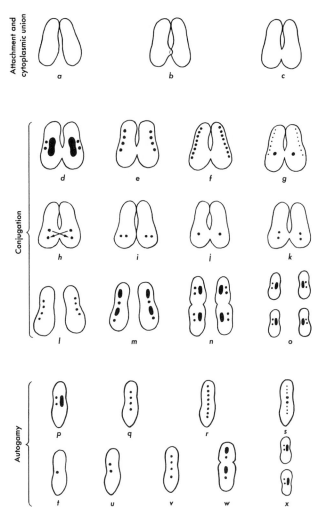

Fig. 5.22.   Conjugation and autogamy in *Paramecium*. The nuclear changes described are those of *P. aurelia*. (a) Attachment between individuals in the "holdfast" region. (b) Development of paroral cones. (c) Cytoplasmic fusion. (d–f) Prior to transfer of pronuclei, meiosis occurs in each conjugant, with the formation of eight haploid nuclei. From this stage onward, the original macronucleus breaks up and disappears; it is omitted in diagrams after (d) for the sake of clarity. (g) Seven of the eight nuclei regress and disappear; the remaining one divides to form migratory and stationary nuclei. (h–j) Each migratory nucleus moves across to the other conjugant and fuses with the recipient's stationary nucleus. (k and l) The fusion nucleus divides mitotically to form four nuclei, and the conjugants separate. (m) In each exconjugant, two nuclei enlarge to form macronuclei. (n and o) By binary fission, two daughter cells are derived from each exconjugant, while the normal complement of two micronuclei per cell is restored. (p–r) The nuclear changes with which autogamy begins are similar to those of conjugation: with two meiotic divisions, eight haploid nuclei are produced. (Macronuclear changes are omitted for the sake of clarity.) (s) Two of the haploid nuclei survive, in contrast to one in conjugation. (t–v) The two nuclei fuse, and the fusion nucleus divides to form four. (w and x) Two of the nuclei become macronuclei, the cells divide, and the normal nuclear number is re-established.

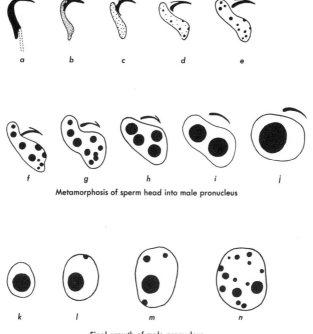

Metamorphosis of sperm head into male pronucleus

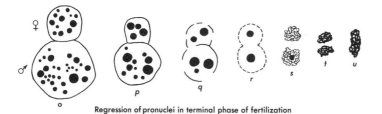

Final growth of male pronucleus

Regression of pronuclei in terminal phase of fertilization

Fig. 5.23.   Pronuclear development in the rat. (a–j) Metamorphosis of the sperm head into a
male pronucleus. There is a great increase in nuclear volume, and nucleoli make their appearance,
grow, and coalesce. The characteristic "rod" of the rat spermatozoon becomes detached as the
pronucleus forms; it disappears during the later phases of fertilization. Simultaneously with the
changes shown here, the female pronucleus develops from the chromosome group left in the egg
after emission of the second polar body: the chromosomes fade from view (as seen in living
eggs examined by phase-contrast microscopy), a nuclear membrane becomes evident, and
nucleoli grow and coalesce, in much the same way as in the male pronucleus. (k–n) Later stages
in the development of the male pronucleus, at a lower magnification than that shown in (a–j).
(o) Male and female pronuclei come together in the middle of the egg; in the rat, the male
pronucleus has about 2.5 times the volume of the female. (p–t) Syngamy concludes with diminution
in nuclear volume and number of nucleoli, disappearance of nuclear membrane and nucleoli,
and reappearance of chromosomes. (u) Paternal and maternal chromosome complements come
together to form the metaphase plate of the first cleavage division. Drawn from photographs
published in J. Roy. Micr. Soc., 71 (1951), 295

remains unchanged in the cytoplasm while the oöcyte completes its development and maturation. Much more commonly, the time of sperm entry is closely associated with that of maturation. In several forms, the germinal vesicle is intact (and usually in the dictyotene stage) at sperm penetration, and the whole of the remaining course of meiosis must ensue before female pronucleus formation. (An analogous situation exists in *Paramecium*, in which attachment between conjugants in the mating reaction precedes, and is considered to be the stimulus for, meiosis.) Alteratively, meiosis proceeds spontaneously to either the first or second metaphase and is held at these points pending sperm penetration; female pronucleus formation necessarily waits upon completion of meiosis. The development of a female pronucleus from a chromosome group seems generally to involve the appearance first of a number of small nuclei (karyomeres) that progressively unite to form the single nucleus. Sometimes male pronucleus formation from the sperm head seems also to occur by fusion of karyomeres.

Properties of pronuclei have attracted attention particularly in mammalian eggs, in which the pronuclear life span is of the order of twelve hours. Male and female pronuclei are of about the same size in many animals, such as the golden hamster, field vole *Microtus agrestis*, ferret, vespertilionid bat, armadillo *Dasypus novemcinctus*, pig, man, wallaby *Setonix*, native cat *Dasyurus*, opossum *Didelphis*, and spiny anteater *Echidna*. In others, there is more noticeable disparity, especially in the rat and mouse in which male pronuclei have two and a half times the volume of female pronuclei. Rodent pronuclei are largest relative to size of egg (nucleocytoplasmic ratio about 1:30; by contrast the figure for the rabbit is 1:90), and have very prominent nucleoli. Studies in the rat have shown that there are two generations of nucleoli: the first group appears directly from the metamorphosing sperm head or the groups of egg chromosomes, and the second arises in association with the nuclear membrane. The primary nucleoli grow and coalesce to form usually a single large nucleolus before the secondary nucleoli start to form. In late pronuclear life, all nucleoli move away from the nuclear membrane and gather near the center of the pronucleus. There is also evidence of a third generation of nucleoli: very small bodies that arise in the nuclear membrane and are then apparently budded off into the cytoplasm, surrounded by an intact single envelope of nuclear membrane. The number of nucleoli in rat egg pronuclei is usually quite large and sometimes exceeds the haploid chromosome number ($n = 21$). Pronuclear nucleoli appear to be devoid of RNA. In the nucleoplasm of pronuclei, the DNA is evidently too dispersed for detection by the usual histochemical methods, except near the beginning and near the end of pronuclear development. The pronuclear phase terminates with diminution in number of nucleoli and size of pronuclei, and finally in the disappearance of these structures and the condensation of the chromosome groups (Fig. 5.23).

There are many variations in the patterns of movements made by pronuclei. In *Paramecium*, the migratory nuclei pass simultaneously but in opposite directions through the same cytoplasmic passage between conjugants. The highly irregular shapes these nuclei exhibit in fixed material suggest that their journey is effected by some form of amoeboid activity (Fig. 5.16). The sperm nuclei in gymnosperms and angiosperms migrate in often complex paths from the point of their release from the pollen tube to the point of nuclear fusion. Movement is evidently rapid and seems not to be due to cytoplasmic movement, for the two sperm nuclei (in angiosperms) take divergent paths, and the tube nucleus and the remains of the synergid nucleus, also commonly deposited in the embryo sac endoplasm, show no definite movements of their own. In some gymnosperms (the ginkgoales and cycads), the male nuclei are incorporated within ciliated sperms having visible motility, but the mechanism whereby the sperm nuclei of other higher plants effect their translation in space is quite unknown.

Mystery also continues to surround the means of pronuclear movement in the eggs of various marine organisms and of urodeles and frogs, to which a great deal of attention has been given. It was early noticed that, in many different forms, the sperm head rotates through an angle of 180° soon after entry into the egg cytoplasm, and a sperm aster appears, centering on the base of the head (Fig. 5.24). As the head develops into a male pronucleus, it migrates, and the sperm aster appears to lead it through the cytoplasm up to the point where union with the female pronucleus is to take place. At the same time, the female pronucleus begins to move and proceeds until it also reaches the point of union. There is definitely a suggestion of interpronuclear influence here; such an influence may be more general: in polyspermic urodele eggs the progress of the extra male pronuclei is halted as soon as the successful male pronucleus meets the female. After union, pronuclei may continue to move until they reach the position of their ultimate breakdown and replacement by chromosomes of the first cleavage spindle (Fig. 5.25). Explanations for a movement mechanism based on an attractive force between the pronuclei or on traction exerted by astral rays have as yet proved inadequate, because they fail to account for many of the pronuclear movements and because experimental removal of either pronucleus does not prevent the other one from following its normal path. Cytoplasmic currents are unlikely to be responsible at any stage, since other organelles do not show the same kind of movement.

With the arrival of the two pronuclei together, further integration

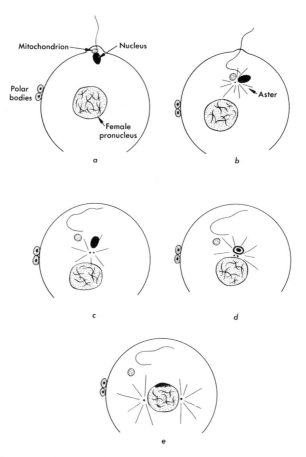

Fig. 5.24. Fertilization in *Arbacia*. When the sperm head has entered the cytoplasm (*a*), it turns through 180° (*b–e*), the sperm aster becomes evident, the midpiece is detached, and the aster seemingly leads the sperm nucleus toward the point of union with the female pronucleus (*c* and *d*). Nuclear union appears to be complete and involves a male pronucleus that has not enlarged appreciably. The sperm aster divides to become the amphiaster for the first cleavage division (*e*).

may or may not take place. In ascomycetes and in the amoeba *Sappinea diploidea*, the conjugants each contain a single pronucleus, and conjugation involves complete cytoplasmic fusion. The pronuclei retain their integrity and lie unchanged, side by side, throughout the life of the zygote. Eventually the organism divides, and at this fission the two pronuclei divide independently so that the daughter cells also have two separate nuclei (each still haploid). It is only when two organisms are in the course of conjugation that the nuclei fuse and then go through two meiosis-like divisions, with the elimination of polar groups of chromatin (Fig. 5.26). The corresponding situation in metazoans is shown by the

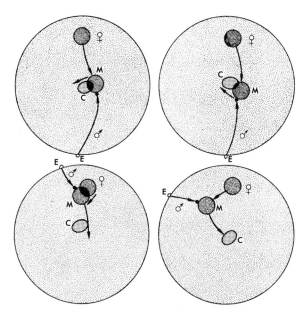

Fig. 5.25. Tracks of the pronuclei in their movements toward each other and to the site of the cleavage nucleus (marked C). E = entrance point of spermatozoon (fertilization cone). ♀ = original position of female pronucleus. ♂ = track of male pronucleus. M = meeting point of the pronuclei. Sea urchin. Redrawn modified from E. B. Wilson, *The Cell in Development and Heredity* (Macmillan, 1928).

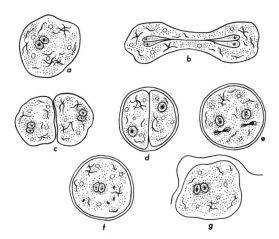

Fig. 5.26. Life cycle of *Sappinea diploidea*. (a) Showing form of organism, with two nuclei in close contact. (b) Binary fission. (c) Start of conjugation. (d) Conjugants become enclosed in a cyst, as the two nuclei in each conjugant fuse to form a single nucleus. (e) Cytoplasmic union is followed by meiosis. (f) Polar chromosome groups regress, and the two newly reduced nuclei come into apposition. (g) Organism emerges from cyst.

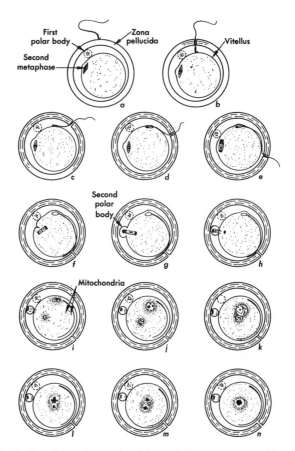

Fig. 5.27. Fertilization of the rat egg. (*a–d*) Entry of the spermatozoon. The shading in the zona pellucida denotes occurrence of the zona reaction. The outline of the first polar body is broken because, in the rat, it commonly disintegrates before ovulation. (*d–h*) Completion of second meiotic division. (*i–l*) Pronuclear development. (*m*) Reappearance of chromosome groups. (*n*) First cleavage metaphase. Redrawn from C. R. Austin and M. W. H. Bishop, *Biol. Rev. Cambr. Philos. Soc.*, 32 (1957), 296.

crustacean *Cyclops*, in which the chromosome groups deriving from the pronuclei become arranged on separate spindles. In *Ascaris* also, the chromosome groups retain their individuality, though they line up on the same first cleavage spindle. In mammals, the pronuclei give rise to two distinct chromosome groups, but there is some suggestion of an intermingling of maternal and paternal chromosomes before the first cleavage anaphase (Figs. 5.23 and 5.27). In most plants and in echinoderms, the pronuclei coalesce to form a single fusion or zygote nucleus, which gives place to a single chromosome group in the prophase of the first cleavage division.

Six

Immediate Consequences
of Fertilization

The female gametes of some plants and animals can proceed with development in the absence of any association with male gametes (see "Meiosis in parthenogenesis" in Chapter 2). But in most organisms the female gametes remain in a state of suspended development and proceed only when gamete union occurs; if this stimulus is lacking, they soon degenerate. The consequences of gamete union in these species are initiated, often dramatically, at cytoplasmic fusion; they take the form of structural and functional changes in the female gamete and collectively characterize the process known as activation. (In *Paramecium*, activation is evidently induced by the initial attachment occurring in the mating reaction; activation therefore precedes cytoplasmic union and is thought to be brought about by the interaction of mating-type substances.) The precise manner in which activation is provoked by the male gamete is still conjectural; the effective stimulus would seem to be nonspecific, for the eggs of several different animals can be activated by a wide variety of artificial agents (heat, cold, hyper- and hypotonic salt solutions, ultraviolet and X-irradiation, acids, alkalis, alkaloids, fat solvents, bile salts, soaps, mechanical agitation, and electric currents). Nor is there a clear conception of just which biochemical changes, of the many known, should be regarded as constituting the essential response to the activating stimulus.

In addition to biochemical changes, various structural changes are often associated with activation, including alterations in shape and size of the female gamete, and in the distribution of its cytoplasmic components. Contemporaneously with these effects, there is evident also the initiation or resumption of meiotic divisions in the maturation of the egg.

The details depend on the stage of meiosis at which development of the female gamete is suspended, and when resumption is involved the subsequent meiotic phases can be regarded as an aspect of activation. For our purposes, however, it seems best to treat maturation separately from the other activation changes noted.

Finally, there is a series of reactions with quite a different connotation; they are concerned chiefly with the prevention of precocious reconjugation, the exclusion of surplus spermatozoa, or the disposal of supernumerary male pronuclei. The first category includes changes underlying loss of mating activity. Reactions in the second category take such forms as extrusion of a jelly coat, elevation of a fertilization membrane, formation of a hyaline layer, occlusion of micropyles, the zona reaction, and the block to polyspermy. Mechanisms in the third category are those that tend to prevent more than one male pronucleus from becoming associated or fusing with the female pronucleus.

General structural and metabolic changes

Changes in the form and physical properties of eggs are of various kinds: streaming of cytoplasm toward the point of sperm attachment; rearrangement in the distribution of cytoplasmic components (Fig. 6.1); changes in over-all shape resembling amoeboid movement (but ending with the assumption of spherical form); variation in the light-scattering power of the cortex (observations indicating either increase or decrease of refractility, depending on the method of examination); increase in membrane capacitance; reduction in volume of the vitellus, ranging from 2 per cent to 25 per cent in different animals (Figs. 6.2, 6.4, and 6.7); and

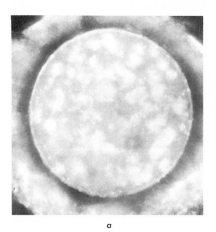 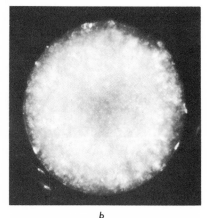

a   *b*

Fig. 6.1   Rabbit eggs as seen when examined in the fresh state by dark-field illumination. (a) Unpenetrated egg. (b) Egg undergoing fertilization; note the rearrangement of refractile particles.

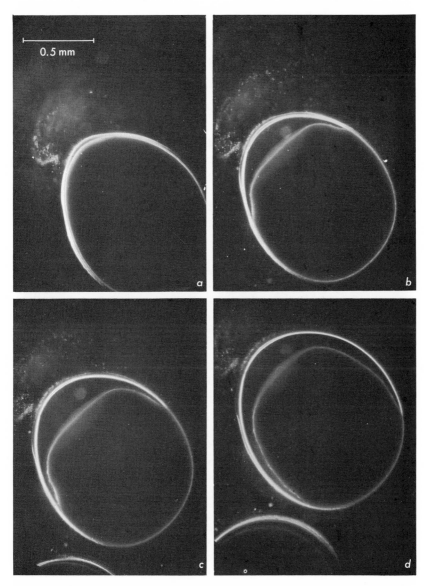

Fig. 6.2. Lamprey eggs, treated with a suspension of spermatozoa and examined by dark-field illumination. Note contraction of vitellus, beginning immediately below the region of the chorion that bears the "tuft" (Fig. 5.4.), through which spermatozoa enter the egg. From R. A. Kille, *Exp. Cell Res.,* 20 (1960), 12.

changes in the viscosity of the cortical cytoplasm (either an increase or a decrease, depending on species and method of study), which appear to be attributable to redistribution of calcium in the cytoplasm. In *Paramecium*, the activation phenomena appropriate for mention here include the initiation of "holdfast" union (arising perhaps from the elaboration of "holdfast" substances), paroral cone formation (essentially a change of shape), and the breakdown of the macronuclei (underlying modifications of metabolism) (Fig. 5.22).

A structural reaction that has long aroused interest is the formation of the fertilization or entry cone (Fig. 5.18). This has been studied especially in the eggs of marine invertebrates, in some of which, as in the starfish, the cone appeared to form before sperm contact with the vitellus (Fig. 5.8). It is now known that the cone arises in response to contact with the acrosome filament and in fact represents egg cytoplasm moving up inside the filament membrane. But fine acrosome filaments like that of the starfish spermatozoon were not clearly recognized until the 1950's; earlier workers were therefore at a loss to account for the means whereby a strand of cytoplasm was projected from the vitellus to meet the spermatozoon in its advance through the jelly coat, and then, in subsiding, was apparently active in drawing the spermatozoon into the vitellus. Different forms of fertilization cone have been described in different animals, and this variation is probably attributable to differences in filament form and the physical properties of the egg cortical cytoplasm. Mammalian eggs, too, develop a kind of fertilization cone—a small mound of cytoplasm at the point of attachment of the sperm head (Fig. 5.27)—and this generally persists for a short while after the head has passed into the vitellus.

Metabolic changes occurring in eggs upon activation have received most attention. The first important metabolic study was on oxygen consumption, and, though there have since been many conflicting results and theories, it is now generally agreed that a large increase in oxygen consumption, incident upon sperm penetration, can consistently be demonstrated in sea-urchin eggs, provided precautions are taken to maintain an environment favorable to the gametes. With similar implications is the evidence that the unpenetrated egg contains a cytochrome-oxidase inhibitor which is inactivated or removed early in fertilization. Protein metabolism also appears to be involved. Unfertilized sea-urchin eggs can utilize glucose for amino acid synthesis or take up amino acids from the medium, but have very little ability to incorporate amino acids into protein. On the other hand, activated eggs, like the early oöcytes from the ovary, are well able to incorporate amino acids into proteins and even effect some protein synthesis. And yet the enzymes involved in protein synthesis have been found by in vitro tests to be just as active when extracted from eggs before sperm penetration as from eggs under-

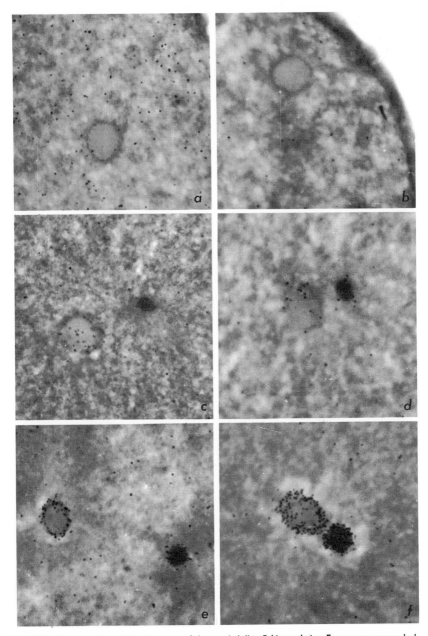

Fig. 6.3. Uptake of thymidine by eggs of the sand dollar *Echinarachnius*. Eggs were suspended for 1 hour in sea water containing tritiated thymidine and then seminated. Sections were examined by autoradiography. (a) Before penetration. (b) Soon after sperm penetration (the head can be seen near the surface). (c and d) 20 minutes, and (e and f) 30 minutes after semination. Labeling is chiefly in the pronuclei and becomes particularly intense as the time of nuclear union approaches. From E. B. Simmel and D. A. Karnofsky, *J. Biophysic. Biochem. Cytol.*, 10:1 (May, 1961), 59–68, by permission of The Rockefeller Institute Press.

going fertilization. Some other part of the system is therefore implicated, and the evidence is that the bar to protein synthesis in the unactivated egg is a suppressed functional state of the messenger RNA or the ribosomes. Other synthetic processes are also held in abeyance before activation, and important among these is that responsible for the DNA augmentation that precedes the first cleavage division. In the sand dollar *Echinarachnius parma*, for example, DNA synthesis as shown by uptake of labeled thymidine is lacking in the nuclei of unactivated eggs but becomes increasingly evident with pronuclear development during fertilization (see Fig. 6.3). Thus the emerging biochemical picture of activation is that of an awakening (possibly a release from inhibition) of both anabolic and catabolic systems.

Maturation

The significance of maturation as the process in which recombination of genes and halving of the chromosome number are effected was discussed under "Meiosis" in Chapter 1 and under "Role of meiosis" in Chapter 2, and the stages of maturation at which gamete fusion takes place in different animals were set out under "Nuclear fusion" in Chapter 5. In most animals, meiosis is arrested at some point pending gamete

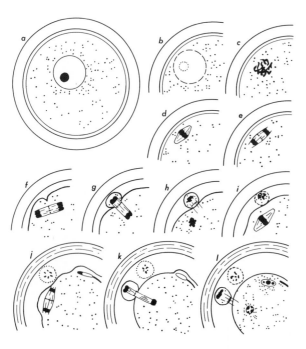

Fig. 6.4. Maturation of the rat egg. (a) Fully grown primary oöcyte. (b) Migration of germinal vesicle to the peripheral cytoplasm, and disappearance of nucleolus and nuclear membrane. (c and d) Prophase and metaphase of the first meiotic division. (e) Anaphase. (f and g) Rotation of the telophase spindle through 90°, and start of polar-body separation. The intermediate body of the spindle is included in the polar body. (h–j) Prophase, metaphase, and anaphase of the second meiotic division, which waits at metaphase for sperm entry to occur. (k and l) Separation of the second polar body. Associated with the emission of both polar bodies there is a contraction of the vitellus, so that the vitelline volume after sperm entry is about 15 per cent less than that in the primary oöcyte. The first polar body generally disintegrates before ovulation. Redrawn from C. R. Austin, *The Mammalian Egg* (Blackwell Scientific Publications, 1961).

fusion and, in these, resumption of meiosis is a distinctive accompaniment of activation.

In the Metazoa, maturation generally entails the production of two polar bodies containing discarded chromosomes; in insects and crustaceans (as in certain ciliates and fungi), such chromosomes form instead polar groups that degenerate and disappear in the peripheral cytoplasm. Both meiotic telophase spindles carry, in many organisms, a distinctive intermediate body containing RNA which is apparently left behind when the chromosomes separate at anaphase. This body is thought to represent surplus nucleic acid, and consistently it is incorporated in the polar bodies, where these are formed. In many eggs forming polar bodies, the meiotic spindles are paratangentially oriented until telophase is reached, after which they rotate through 90° to occupy a radial position; rotation seems to play a part in the process of polar body separation (Fig. 6.4). The first polar body often undergoes division, so that the total number of polar bodies becomes three (as in many marine invertebrates and amphibians); alternatively, the first polar body may soon regress and break up, so that only one polar body is seen at the end of maturation (as in several mammals). The size of polar bodies varies considerably— relatively small in megalecithal eggs and relatively large in microlecithal eggs. Sometimes, "giant" polar bodies are formed and may even be equal in size to the remainder of the vitellus; more information on this anomaly is given under "Partial fertilization" in Chapter 7.

Loss of mating activity

In *Paramecium*, a refractory period follows a mating event, and in such a period further mating reactions cannot be evoked. The loss is seen also after autogamy and, under certain circumstances, after a mating reaction between living and dead individuals. Enucleate fragments of paramecia, too, can be shown to lose mating reactivity, after undergoing the initial aggregation with normal animals, so the loss is not dependent upon the nuclear changes of activation.

In some angiosperms, the pollen tube deposits its nuclei in a synergid cell, which is destroyed when it discharges the nuclei into the embryo sac; consequently, the synergid cell is not available should another pollen tube arrive. Moreover, if a second pollen tube should enter the other synergid, no reaction follows.

Exclusion of surplus spermatozoa

The classic example of a sperm-excluding mechanism is the elevation of the fertilization membrane, a process that is known in the eggs of some annelids, sea urchins, starfish, the lancelet *Branchiostoma*, and the frog. As noted earlier, the sea-urchin egg, before sperm entry, has a compound vitelline membrane some 150 to 200 Å thick that appears to consist of two unit membranes in close apposition. Data from electron micrographs can be interpreted to signify that the inner membrane is reflected around cortical granules (0.5 to 1.3 μ in diameter), large numbers of which are disposed immediately below the cell surface (Fig. 6.5). At sperm contact with the vitellus, the cortical granules in the immediate vicinity appear suddenly to break through their retaining membrane ("explode"); this reaction is propagated over the cortex so that it eventually involves all, or most of, the granules. The granule material (mucoprotein in nature) thus released becomes applied to the outer membrane, increasing its thickness greatly. The augmented membrane, now termed the fertilization membrane, rises from the egg surface, apparently through the accumulation of fluid beneath it, an effect attributed to the osmotic action of substances emitted with the reacting cortical granules. The invaginations of the inner membrane are eliminated so that it flattens out as a smooth plasma membrane over the vitelline surface. At the same time, an additional, homogeneous coating makes its appearance over the plasma membrane, and this is called the hyaline layer. The fertilization membrane achieves a final thickness of about 800 Å; its impermeability to spermatozoa constitutes a lasting barrier against polyspermy, but because of its relatively slow rate of formation, *initial* protection must reside in some other mechanism. This is almost certainly the change, to be considered shortly, known as the fast component of the block to polyspermy.

In *Nereis* and *Platynereis*, the vitelline membrane is also a double structure, but the fertilization membrane is derived in a rather different manner. The cortex of the egg is arranged in the form of compartments or alveoli, which are packed with large numbers of granular bodies. Following initial sperm contact with the vitellus, the cortical alveoli break down and release the granules, which, apparently becoming hydrated, swell enormously to make a jellylike material. The jelly flows out from the egg until there is a thick coating over the surface, impervious to spermatozoa. With the collapse of cortical alveoli, the surface of the egg cytoplasm, lined by the inner layer of vitelline membrane (now the plasma membrane), falls away, leaving the outer layer as the fertilization membrane (Fig. 6.6).

Exclusion of surplus spermatozoa from sturgeon and teleost eggs seems to be due mainly to properties of the micropyle. The micropylar canal is so narrow that only one spermatozoon at a time is able to pass through. When the first has entered the cytoplasm of the egg, a gelatinous substance flows up the canal, pushing the other spermatozoa out and forming a permanent plug. A wave of contraction then passes over the vitellus, and subsequently a layer, resembling in appearance

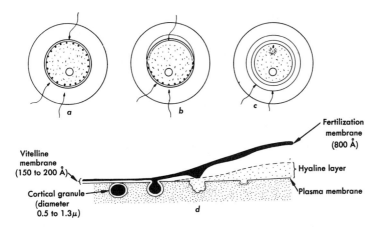

Fig. 6.5. (a–c) The course of events in cortical-granule breakdown and fertilization-membrane elevation in the sea-urchin egg. (d) Mechanism inferred to underlie these events.

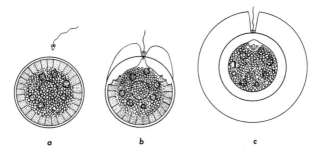

Fig. 6.6. Reaction of the *Nereis* egg to sperm penetration. (a) The cortex of the egg contains many alveoli filled with fine granular material. (b and c) At sperm penetration, the alveoli break down, and the granular material, apparently becoming strongly hydrated, swells to form a thick jelly coat that eventually surrounds the egg.

and imperviousness to spermatozoa the hyaline layer of the sea-urchin egg, forms on the surface of the vitellus. In addition to these changes, other reactions are seen, which however do not seem directly concerned with sperm exclusion: the breakdown of cortical alveoli and the hardening of the chorion. The cortical alveoli (quite different in kind from the nereid alveoli) are small, vesicular structures about 7 to 13 μ in diameter and contain a mucopolysaccharide; they are found in lamprey eggs as well as those of bony fishes. At sperm entry, a wave of alveolar breakdown passes around the vitellus; the alveoli apparently discharge their contents into the perivitelline space. The substance released by the cortical alveoli is thought, by virtue of its osmotic properties, to

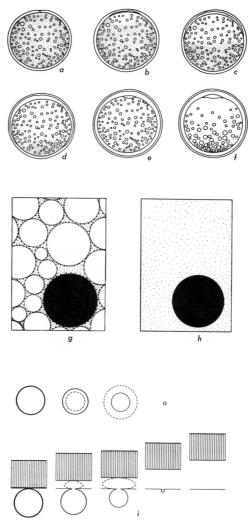

Fig. 6.7. Early changes in a fish egg—that of the medaka *Oryzias latipes*—following sperm penetration. (*a–f*) The chorion and vitellus separate, first in the micropylar region and then progressively over the whole egg. The cortical alveoli (stipple) break down and disappear, and this change too is propagated over the egg. The lipid droplets (small circles) gather near the vegetal pole. (*g* and *h*) Appearance of part of the egg surface, before and after alveolar breakdown. White circles represent cortical alveoli and the black circle a lipid droplet. The large dots represent the so-called a-granules that also disappear after sperm penetration and that may be zymogen granules, the active enzyme being possibly responsible for the alveolar change. (*i*) Scheme to explain alveolar breakdown, showing how an alveolus might empty its contents between plasma membrane and chorion; through their hydrophilic property, the colloids released from the alveolus could greatly increase the free fluid there and thus produce a wide perivitelline space. The upper series represents the surface view and the lower the sectional view. The chorion is distinguished by vertical shading. Redrawn from T. Yamamoto, *Intern. Rev. Cytol.,* 12 (1961), 361.

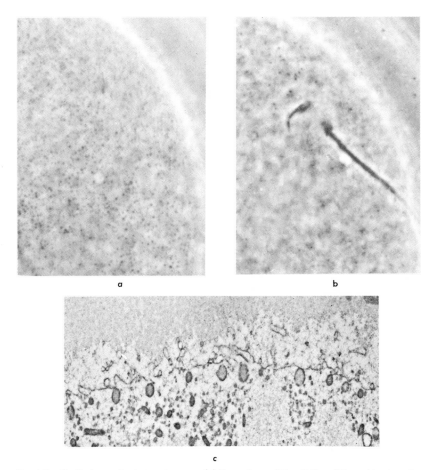

a   b

c

Fig. 6.8.   Cortical granules in hamster eggs. (a) The surface of the vitellus of the golden-hamster egg, showing the numerous granules that can be seen before sperm penetration. (b) After sperm penetration, the great majority of these granules disappear. Phase-contrast pictures of living eggs. (c) Electron micrograph of the cortex of a golden-hamster egg in which can be discerned several large granular bodies lying immediately below the plasma membrane. These are not to be found in penetrated eggs. (a and b) from C. R. Austin, *Exp. Cell Res.,* 10 (1956), 537.

be responsible for increase in the perivitelline space and distention of the chorion, and also for the characteristic hardening of the chorion that occurs in fish and lamprey eggs after sperm penetration (Fig. 6.7).

In many algae, mosses, and ferns, the egg cell is known to become surrounded by a cell wall after fertilization, but precisely what the normal protection against polyspermy may be has not yet been elucidated.

The most rapid change offering resistance to the entry of surplus spermatozoa is the block to polyspermy, the existence of which can be demonstrated by determining the incidence of polyspermy exhibited by eggs treated experimentally with sperm suspensions of different density. The change is propagated over the egg cortex from the point of original sperm attachment. In the sea urchin, evidence indicates that the change is diphasic, with a fast component, which confers partial protection, covering the egg surface in one or two seconds, and a slower complete block that is established in about sixty seconds. The fast change is in effect the loss from the vitelline surface of the capacity to form attachment with spermatozoa, and as yet no morphological change in the egg cortex has been unequivocally linked with it. The slow component is probably attributable to the formation of the fertilization membrane. The fast block is evidently transient in nature, for removal of the fertilization membrane permits the egg to be entered by a second spermatozoon (see "Refertilization" in Chapter 7).

In several mammals (such as the rat, mouse, rabbit, mole, and pocket gopher), a block to polyspermy seems to play a significant role, for surplus ("supplementary") spermatozoa are often found in the perivitelline space of eggs undergoing fertilization. The eggs of many other mammals (golden hamster, Chinese hamster, field vole, Libyan jird, dog, sheep, pig, and apparently man), however, very rarely exhibit supplementary spermatozoa and must possess a mechanism that tends to prevent extra spermatozoa from even entering the perivitelline space. In these animals, it is clear that a change occurs in the zona pellucida that renders it impermeable to spermatozoa, and this is termed the zona reaction. Though supplementary spermatozoa are encountered in the eggs of rats and mice, their frequency distribution shows that a zona reaction is operative here too, though of a lower efficiency than the zona reaction in the second group of mammals. Thus mammalian eggs possess two protective devices against polyspermy that differ in their relative importance in different species. The zona reaction, like the block to polyspermy, has the characteristics of a propagated change, but its precise mechanism is still a subject for speculation. Cortical granules

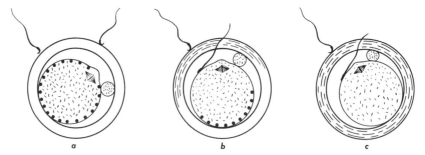

Fig. 6.9.   Possible mechanism of the zona reaction in the golden-hamster egg. (a) Approach of fertilizing spermatozoon. (b and c) Contact of the sperm head with the vitelline surface causes breakdown of the cortical granules in the immediate vicinity, and the reaction is then propagated over the whole vitellus. Substances released by the reaction diffuse across the perivitelline space and act upon the zona pellucida, rendering this membrane impermeable to further spermatozoa. Redrawn from C. R. Austin, *The Mammalian Egg* (Blackwell Scientific Publications, 1961).

(0.1 to 0.5 μ in diameter) have been found in the eggs of the golden hamster, rat, mouse, guinea pig, rabbit, coypu, and pig; these granules disappear after sperm penetration (Fig. 6.8). It is possible that the granule change, like that underlying the elevation of the fertilization membrane, traverses the cortex from the point of sperm entry and results in the release of a membrane-modifying agent (Fig. 6.9). In this way a progressive change in the zona pellucida could be brought about. The rabbit egg, however, fails to evince a zona reaction, although it possesses cortical granules.

Disposal of supernumerary male pronuclei

It seems characteristic of certain eggs, such as those of some angiosperms, a few insects, and apparently all elasmobranchs, urodeles, reptiles, and birds, that surplus spermatozoa are normally not excluded from entering the egg cytoplasm and there forming pronuclei. The phenomenon is referred to as physiological polyspermy (as opposed to pathological polyspermy, which occurs as a comparatively rare event in eggs that normally exclude surplus spermatozoa—see "Polyspermy"

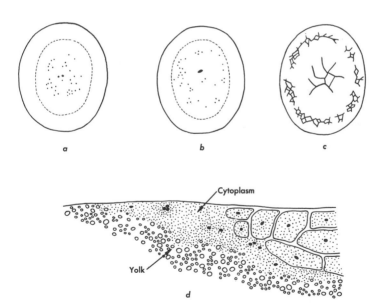

Fig. 6.10. Accessory nuclei and cleavage in the pigeon's egg. (a) Plan view of the blastodisc showing male and female pronuclei in syngamy in the center, surrounded by the accessory (supernumerary) male pronuclei. (b) Slightly later stage: fusion nucleus in the center and the accessory nuclei moving toward the periphery of blastodisc. (c) Primary cleavage lines of the developing embryo in the middle while accessory cleavage occurs around the edge of the blastodisc. (d) Section through the blastodisc edge showing some cell formation and several free nuclei. Redrawn from E. H. Harper, *Am. J. Anat.*, 3 (1904), 349.

in Chapter 7). In physiological polyspermy, union of more than one male pronucleus with the female (polyandry) is most uncommon, because the supernumerary male pronuclei are suppressed or rejected when the successful one becomes associated with the female pronucleus. Suppression has been most clearly demonstrated in urodeles, in the eggs of some of which the inhibitory effect appears to originate in the vicinity of the conjugating pronuclei and then to pass outward, overwhelming progressively all the other male pronuclei. Rejection is seen best in bird eggs, in which the surplus male pronuclei are relegated to the periphery of the blastodisc where some of them induce cell division in the early cleavage stages of embryonic development (Fig. 6.10).

SEVEN

Unusual and Abnormal Forms
of Fertilization

Fertilization, considered in its simplest terms as the cytoplasmic and nuclear union of two cells, is a sufficiently complex cytological phenomenon to be subject to modification or error in quite a variety of ways. In addition, further complication arises in many organisms because cytoplasmic union occurs before or during oöcyte maturation (see "Nuclear union" in Chapter 5), and maturation, with its two meiotic divisions, is an important source of unusual or abnormal events (Table 7.1). Among the more common variations of the fertilization pattern are those involving numbers of pronuclei: (1) the fusion of two or more male gametes with the female gamete (a condition known in many animals as polyspermy), which initiates the formation of two or more male pronuclei; (2) the development of two or more male pronuclei, leading to union of these with the female pronucleus (polyandrous syngamy or polyandry); (3) the failure of emission of the first or second polar body, with the result that the male pronucleus unites with two female pronuclei (polygyny); (4) the nonparticipation of the male pronucleus in fertilization, after activation of the female gamete (gynogenesis); and (5) the nonparticipation of the female pronucleus, the male pronucleus being alone involved in subsequent development (androgenesis). (6) Akin to polyspermy and polyandry is the situation in which, some time after the initiation of normal fertilization, one or more additional male gametes fuse with the female (refertilization); here again, as in (1) and (2), two or more male pronuclei become involved, but in this instance they are of different ages. (7) A variation of a different kind is seen when the male pronucleus fails for one reason or another to meet the female pronucleus, and eventually unites with a

Table 7.1. Forms of maturation or fertilization on which observations have been recorded in mammals, and the furthest advance of embryonic development seen.

1st polar body	2nd polar body	Pronuclei	1st cleavage	Type of development	Chromosomal status	Furthest advance	
						Established	Uncertain
+	+	1♀ 1♂	+	Normal	Diploidy	Birth	
+	+	1♀ 2♂	+	Polyandry	Triploidy	Implantation	Birth
+	+	1♀ 1+1♂		Refertilization	Triploidy	Pronuclei	
+	+	1♀ 3♂		Polyandry	Tetraploidy	Pronuclei	
+	-	2♀ 1♂	+	Polygyny	Triploidy	Implantation	Birth
+ or -	- or +	2♀ 2♂		Polyandry and polygyny	Tetraploidy	Pronuclei	
+	+	1♀ 0♂	+	Parthenogenesis	Haploidy	Cleavage	
+	-	2♀ 0♂	+	Parthenogenesis	Diploidy	Implantation	
+	-	2♀ 0♂	-	Parthenogenesis	Tetraploidy		Blastocyst
-	-	?4♀ 0♂	+	Parthenogenesis	Tetraploidy		Birth
+	+	1♀ (1♂)	+	Gynogenesis	Haploidy		Cleavage spindle
+	+	(1♀) 1♂	+	Androgenesis	Haploidy		Cleavage spindle
+	-*	2♀ 0♂	+	Immediate cleavage	Haploidy	2-cell oötid	Cleavage
+	-*	2♀ 1♂	+	Immediate cleavage and partial fertilization	Haplodiploidy	2-cell oötid	Cleavage
-*	+	2♀ 0♂	+	Immediate cleavage	Haploidy	2-cell oötid	

+ = occurs
- = inhibited
* Polar spindle cleaves egg.

blastomere nucleus of the two-cell or four-cell egg (partial fertilization). (8) Much later embryonic stages have also been said to be subject to sperm penetration, and there is little doubt that penetration may occur into cells of the female genital tract, though nuclear syngamy is not known to ensue (somatic fertilization). (9) Finally, there remains to be considered the occurrence of fertilization in an abnormal location, namely the fertilization in vitro of eggs that under natural conditions are fertilized within the animal body. This is essentially an experimental maneuver; its importance in the present context is that it makes possible a clearer definition of the range of environmental change permitting normal fertilization.

Polyspermy

It is usual and evidently normal for many spermatozoa to enter large yolky eggs, such as those of birds, reptiles, and elasmobranchs, and for several spermatozoa to enter moderately yolk-laden eggs, such as those of urodeles and some insects, and even the small, relatively yolk-free eggs of bryozoans. This is known as physiological polyspermy, and its biological advantage may lie in improvement in the chances of syngamy, which might otherwise be poor, particularly in the heavily yoked eggs. By contrast, the female gametes of most animals and plants do not normally undergo fusion with more than one male gamete; when multiple fusion does occur, the state of pathological polyspermy is said to be initiated (Table 7.2). This condition has been studied most extensively in the eggs of sea urchins and certain mammals. Observations of sea-urchin eggs have shown that polyspermy can be induced by placing eggs with dense suspensions of spermatozoa, by seminating immature or aging ("stale") eggs, or by treating eggs with toxic or narcotic agents (notably nicotine, chloral hydrate, and alkaloids), or with heat or cold just before semination. Immature and aged eggs evidently have a slow and therefore inefficient block to polyspermy, and it is surmised that the chemical agents and abnormal temperatures have their effect by interfering with the block mechanism. Investigations have revealed essentially similar conditions in other marine invertebrates and in anurans. In mammals, mating late in oestrus (by which time the eggs are becoming aged) leads to a higher rate of polyspermy, the incidence varying with species and with strains within species. Frequencies as high as 9 per cent have been observed in rats and 10 per cent in pigs, compared with less than 2 per cent when mating occurs early in oestrus. Application of heat to the Fallopian tube or elevation of the general body temperature shortly after ovulation also raises the polyspermy rate, and a figure as high as 34 per cent has been noted in rats.

Table 7.2.   Forms of polyspermy.

Type	Number of sperms entering	Fate of extra male pronuclei	First cleavage spindle	Outcome	Organisms
Physiological	Several	Suppressed	Normal	Normal	Urodeles Bryozoa Angiosperms Some insects*
	Many	Repelled to periphery of blastodisc	Normal	Normal (possibly some mosaicism)	Elasmobranchs Reptiles Birds
	Several	Repelled to periphery of blastodisc	Normal	Normal	Arachnids
Pathological	Two; rarely three or more†	Polyandry	Multipolar	Random distribution of chromosomes during cleavage; development fails to pass blastula stage	Sea urchins Fish (sturgeons)
			Bipolar	Triploid embryo; full development	Angiosperms (occasionally)
			Bipolar	Triploid embryo; development fails to proceed beyond mid-pregnancy	Mammals
		Form separate division centers	Several	Haplodiploid embryos, of which about 10% develop to tadpoles	Frogs
		Fuse with synergids or antipodal cells		Multiple embryos	Angiosperms (occasionally)

* It seems probable that polyspermy is pathological in most insects.   † Numbers are higher under some experimental conditions.

There are several possible consequences of polyspermy. In birds, reptiles, and elasmobranchs, all spermatozoa entering form pronuclei, but only one of the male pronuclei unites with the female. The others become relegated to the periphery of the blastodisc where many degenerate, though some give rise to accessory cleavage in that region (Fig. 6.10). In urodeles and some insects, pronuclei are formed, but the supernumerary ones degenerate before the first cleavage (Fig. 7.1); in Bryozoa, the extra spermatozoa apparently regress before pronucleus formation. Pronuclear degeneration in some urodele eggs seems to be attributable to an inhibitory agent emanating from the fusing male

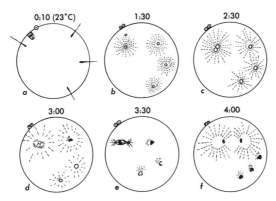

Fig. 7.1.   Polyspermy in the urodele *Triton.* (a) Entry of spermatozoa. The egg is in the metaphase of the second meiotic division. (Time 0 hours 10 minutes after semination; temperature of medium 23° C). (b–d) For the first 2 hours 20 minutes all pronuclei develop similarly, and then, with one male pronucleus involved in syngamy with the female, the supernumerary male pronuclei begin to regress, the nearest one showing the change first. (e and f) As the first cleavage mitosis proceeds, 3 hours 20 minutes to 3 hours 50 minutes after semination, suppression of all supernumerary male pronuclei is completed. Redrawn from G. Fankhauser, *Ann. N. Y. Acad. Sci.,* 49 (1948), 686.

and female pronuclei (or their immediate vicinity), for the nearer supernumerary pronuclei become suppressed first. Thus, the eggs of animals exhibiting physiological polyspermy evidently possess cytoplasmic mechanisms that generally preclude polyandry or serious interference with the cleavage pattern. By contrast, eggs in which polyspermy is pathological seem to depend entirely on means for preventing multiple sperm entry; in these eggs, formation of supernumerary pronuclei leads apparently inevitably to abnormal embryonic development. In sea urchins, polyandry generally ensues, but sometimes supernumerary male pronuclei give rise to accessory cleavage spindles, and cleavage then leads to the development of haploid-diploid embryos of low viability. In fish (sturgeons), the outcome of polyspermy has been found regularly to be polyandry. In anurans, the supernumerary male pronuclei remain separate from one another and from the united male and female pronuclei, and spindles arise in association with each; at the first cleavage, the egg divides into several blastomeres, the number corresponding to the total number of male pronuclei, and further development produces an embryo that is a haploid-diploid mosaic. About 10 per cent of these embryos advance to the tadpole stage, but none are known to have survived to maturity. In mammals, polyspermy has consistently been found to lead to polyandry.

In angiosperms, more than one pollen tube may enter the embryo sac—sometimes as many as twenty do—but not all may open. When several tubes release their nuclei into the sac, the surplus nuclei generally degenerate; rarely, surplus male pronuclei persist, and two of them fuse with the oösphere. A similar result can follow entry into the embryo sac of a single pollen tube containing more than two male nuclei (as many as eight has been recorded). Polyspermy in plants can lead to consequences other than polyandry, and the principal one is the development of multiple embryos. The extra embryos arise from the union of extra male nuclei with the synergids or with the antipodal cells; sometimes the polar nuclei contribute by fusing with separate male nuclei.

In *Chlamydomonas*, a condition analogous to polyspermy is occasionally seen in the fusion of three individuals; some of the resulting triple zygotes are fertile. Triple mating groups are known also in *Paramecium*, but here nuclear exchange occurs only between two conjugants; the third animal, which is usually attached to the posterior end of one of a normal pair of conjugants, undergoes autogamy (Fig. 5.22).

Polyandry

The conjugation of two or more male pronuclei with the female pronucleus is the usual consequence of polyspermy in sea urchins (and in the polychaete worm *Pectinaria*—Fig. 7.2) and mammals (Fig. 7.3), and the occasional one in angiosperms. But the events that follow are different in each of these groups. In sea urchins, the influence of the sperm centrioles is predominant, and when two male pronuclei unite with the female, a tripolar or tetrapolar first-cleavage spindle is formed and the mitosis gives rise to three or four blastomeres. The chromosome distribution is most irregular, and the blastomeres come to have an almost random share of the chromosome complement. This condition is passed on at each subsequent cleavage, and development rarely goes further than the blastula stage. In mammals, too, polyandry

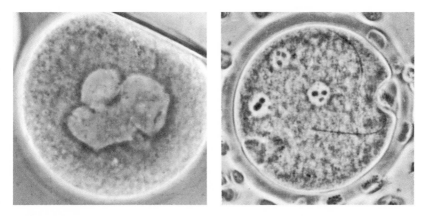

Fig. 7.2. (*left*) Polyandry in *Pectinaria*, with two large male pronuclei in contact with a small female pronucleus. (*right*) Polyandry in the golden-hamster egg. The pronuclei are all about the same size so that polygyny might be suspected, but the presence of two polar bodies and two sperm tails in the vitellus makes the nature of the anomaly clear.

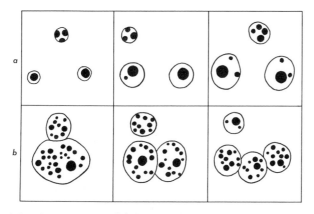

Fig. 7.3. Polyandry in rat eggs. (*a*) Stages in the simultaneous development of one female and two male pronuclei (in each egg, the presence of two sperm tails in the vitellus supported the diagnosis of polyandry, which was based also on the fact that, for most of its development, the male pronucleus is more than twice the size of the female). (*b*) Fully grown male and female pronuclei in eggs exhibiting normal fertilization and two orders of polyandry. As the number of male pronuclei increases, the volume achieved by both male and female pronuclei diminishes, presumably owing to substrate limitations. Drawn from photographs published in *Australian J. Biol. Sci.*, 6 (1953), 674.

is lethal, but the details of development are different. Mammalian sperm centrioles apparently play no role in the formation of the first cleavage spindle, for this spindle in polyandrous eggs is almost invariably bipolar, and the first and subsequent cleavage divisions proceed quite normally. The embryo is, however, triploid in chromosomal constitution (polyandry is one of the principal causes of triploidy— Table 7.3), and this state (for a reason as yet unknown) has proved to be inconsistent with development beyond the midpoint of pregnancy (Table 7.2). Indeed, in mammals there are only two or three cases (human subjects) in which survival of a triploid to postnatal life has been recorded. Higher orders of polyandry in a mammal (rat) are also known, involving three (Fig. 7.3), four, or even five male pronuclei, but the outcome of these states has not been determined. In angiosperms, polyandry also gives a triploid embryo (presumably by way of a bipolar first cleavage spindle), but triploidy in plants does not constitute a bar to full development, and, for the survival of the individual, polyandry is therefore not of critical importance.

Table 7.3.   Possible sources of triploidy in mammals.

	Forms of syngamy leading to triploidy (+)		
Origin of anomaly	*Polyandry*	*Polygyny*	*Aneugamy**
Polyspermy	+	—	—
Polar-body suppression	—	+	—
Binuclear oöcyte	—	[+]†	—
Meiosis suppression	—	—	+
Octaploid oöcyte	—	—	[+]
Diploid spermatozoon	—	—	[+]

Pronuclear constitution

	Polyandry	Polygyny	Aneugamy
Male	● ●	●	● 2n or ●
Female	●	● ●	●	● 2n

* Fertilization involving development of a diploid pronucleus in addition to a normal haploid pronucleus.
† Brackets indicate less likely origins.

Polygyny

Fertilization involving the trinuclear state, wherein two female pronuclei unite with a male pronucleus, has been studied in fewer organisms than has polyandry. It arises through suppression of the first or second polar body; the meiotic division concerned proceeds to telophase, and both groups of chromosomes are retained within the egg. As a result, the embryo has a triploid chromosome complement (Table 7.3). Theoretically, suppression of both polar bodies is possible, giving rise to four female pronuclei, but such an occurrence has not yet been reported.

Instances of "spontaneous" polygyny are known in some marine invertebrates, such as the sea urchin *Arbacia* and the polychaete worm *Pectinaria* (Fig. 7.4). In the urodele *Triturus*, heat treatment of the egg causes submergence of the second polar spindle, so that polar body formation cannot occur and both chromosome groups give rise to female pronuclei. At fertilization, the male pronucleus unites with both female pronuclei, a bipolar spindle is produced, and early development is apparently normal, despite the triploidy; degeneration, however, occurs before maturity. Among mammals, polygyny has been found

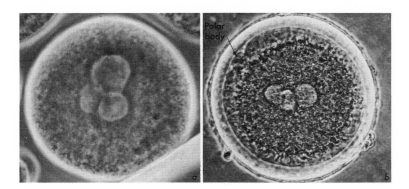

Fig. 7.4. (a) Polygyny in *Pectinaria*: one large male and two small female pronuclei, and the egg displayed only one polar body, whereas two were regularly present with normal fertilization. (b) Presumptive polygyny in the rabbit egg: one large and two small pronuclei (probably male and female, respectively), and only one polar body. In the rabbit, the first polar body survives ovulation often but not always. From C. R. Austin, *J. Cellular Comp. Physiol.*, **56**, Suppl. 1 (1960), 7.

especially in rabbits (Fig. 7.4) and pigs, after mating or artificial insemination late in oestrus; the incidence in pigs (up to 20 per cent) was high enough to represent a significant contribution to the toll of prenatal mortality. In mice, there is evidence that the spontaneous failure of emission of the first or second polar body is controlled by the genotype of the female.

Gynogenesis

This condition is allied to parthenogenesis in that the spermatozoon serves only to activate the egg and plays no further part in fertilization, nor contributes to the genetic constitution of the embryo. Gynogenesis occurs naturally in nematodes such as *Rhabditis aberrans* (for which reason the process is also referred to as nematode pseudogamy), and in planarians such as *Polycelis* spp.; diploidy is achieved through meiosis suppression. Another form of gynogenesis is seen in certain spider beetles: in the triploid species *Ptinus latro*, males are lacking, and development of the eggs, which undergo no chromosome reduction, can only proceed if they are penetrated and activated by spermatozoa of the closely related diploid *P. hirtellus*. Analogous to this is the condition known in a teleost fish, the Amazon molly *Poecilia formosa*, a species that apparently exists solely as females. Mating occurs with other species of this genus whose spermatozoa merely activate the eggs; development is diploid, but it is uncertain what modification of meiosis makes this possible.

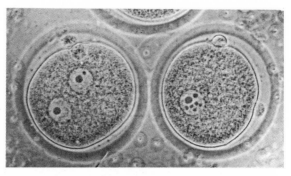

Fig. 7.5.   Rudimentary gynogenesis in the golden hamster. Normal egg on the left. The egg on the right has a sperm tail in the vitellus, a single pronucleus, and two polar bodies; on closer examination, metamorphosis of the sperm head into a male pronucleus was found to have halted at an early stage.

Experimentally, it has been demonstrated that the eggs of the sea urchin *Parechinus* can be entered and activated by spermatozoa of the mussel *Mytilus* or the annelid *Adouinia*; the eggs of the frog *Hyla* can be activated by spermatozoa of the toad *Bufo*; and the eggs of *Bufo* activated by spermatozoa of the salamander *Triton*. In each case, there is chromosome reduction but no pronuclear syngamy, so that the embryos are haploid. In *Parechinus*, these embryos soon degenerate but, in *Hyla* and *Bufo*, tadpoles, albeit of reduced viability, are developed.

A few examples of rudimentary gynogenesis have been reported in mammals, but development seems likely to be very limited (Fig. 7.5).

Some angiosperms also show forms of gynogenesis. Thus, in *Solanum nigrum* pollinated with pollen from *S. luteum*, one or both male nuclei may enter the egg, but no syngamy occurs, and the male nuclei subsequently degenerate. The embryo can, however, develop apparently normally, either as a haploid or a diploid (diploidy coming from suppression of cell-wall formation after the first proembryonic mitosis).

Androgenesis

There do not appear to be any examples of protracted development by androgenesis in any animal, but limited androgenetic development has been provoked in the annelid *Chaetopterus*, in frogs and toads, and in mammals, by treating eggs with X- and ultraviolet irradiation, various dyes, and radiomimetic agents. A few instances of rudimentary spontaneous androgenesis have been recorded in rat and mouse eggs; there was a suggestion that higher incidences occurred in outbred stocks, as compared to inbred strains, and when eggs were fertilized late in their fertile life. All the androgenones so far mentioned were haploid in genotype, but diploid hybrid embryos have been obtained in the moth by crossing *Bombyx mandarina* and *B. mori*, and treating the eggs with temperature shock and X-irradiation.

In plants, occasional androgenetic haploids and diploids have been reported from time to time among the results of hybridization experiments. Typically, the plant androgenetic hybrid shows the features only of the pollen-donor species; in animals, by contrast, there is often evidence of a matriclinous phenotype, testifying to the persistence of maternal genetic influence in the cytoplasm.

Refertilization

When the eggs of the echiuroid worm *Urechis caupo* were treated with acidified sea water after sperm entry but before elevation of the fertilization membrane, membrane elevation was inhibited, and the eggs returned to the unfertilized state (pronuclear development did not proceed). They could now be entered by a second spermatozoon and, in the absence of further treatment, would proceed with fertilization, which would involve polyandry. Treatment with acidified sea water could be applied a second time and the entry of a third spermatozoon thus obtained. A similar result was produced in sea-urchin eggs, by treatment with calcium-free or magnesium-free sea water before fertilization-membrane elevation, or simply by mechanical or enzymatic removal of the membrane. Demembranated eggs were generally entered by several spermatozoa on semination, and the observations suggest that the block to polyspermy is a transient protective mechanism, lasting protection coming from the fertilization membrane.

Refertilization of rat eggs has been obtained by injecting versene solutions into the Fallopian tube shortly after the normal time of sperm penetration. In some instances, the spermatozoon of a secondary penetration failed to form a pronucleus and degenerated, whereas in others, an extra male pronucleus developed: the result presumably depended upon the interval between primary and secondary penetrations.

Partial fertilization

In some sea-urchin eggs, the male pronucleus has been observed to lag behind the sperm aster in its advance to the female pronucleus, and the first cleavage occurred without participation of male chromosomes. The male pronucleus remained unchanged until it united with the nucleus of a blastomere at the two-cell, four-cell or eight-cell stage. The embryo so formed was accordingly a mosaic, some (usually most) cells being haploid and some diploid, bearing both maternal and paternal chromosome complements.

The possibility of a form of partial fertilization has been demonstrated in mice. Both as a result of experimental heat treatment and spontaneously, apparently under the influence of a maternal gene, eggs occasionally failed to produce a second polar body, and the second maturation spindle behaved instead like a cleavage spindle, bisecting the entire egg. The process was termed immediate cleavage; the products closely resembled two-cell eggs with a vesicular nucleus in each "blastomere." In some instances, such an egg was entered by a spermatozoon that formed a male pronucleus in one "blastomere." The eggs seemed normal in general respects, and there appeared to be good chances that some further development could ensue.

The term *partial fertilization* has also been used to refer to a different phenomenon. If sea-urchin eggs are drawn into a capillary tube, so that they are constricted into a cylindrical shape, and warmed slightly, and then spermatozoa are introduced into one end of the tube, sperm entry occurs, but breakdown of the cortical granules and elevation of the fertilization membrane cease at a point along the cylindrical part of the egg. Other changes associated with the response to sperm penetration, such as contraction of the vitellus, formation of the hyaline layer, and cortical migration of pigment granules, are similarly inhibited. If the female pronucleus is in the activated portion of the egg, fertilization can proceed here and is followed by initiation of the first cleavage division, but the cleavage furrow fails to enter the unactivated region. Indeed, the egg is only partially fertilized, and the unactivated portion can be penetrated by a spermatozoon an hour or more after the initial entry. Partial fertilization, in this sense, can also be achieved without use of a capillary tube by treating eggs at the right moment with moderate heat or with nicotine.

Somatic fertilization

Fertilization in angiosperms is characterized by the involvement of two male nuclei, one of which unites with the oösphere nucleus and the other with two polar nuclei (or their fusion product, the pri-

mary endosperm nucleus). The second union forms the triploid endosperm nucleus, which now undergoes several mitotic divisions so that
a number of triploid nuclei come to lie free in the cytoplasm of the
megaspore. Cell walls develop around each of the endosperm nuclei,
and within these cells food materials accumulate. Thus the endosperm
is established; it is not part of the embryo at all but functions as an
important food store for the developing embryo in many plants.

In a sense, union of a male nucleus with the primary endosperm
nucleus is somatic fertilization, and many investigators have sought
to find the equivalent process in animals in the belief that it represents
a method (alternative to gametic fertilization) whereby hereditary
factors are transmitted between individuals. There were indeed re-
ports that, following mating in several vertebrates, many spermatozoa
could be demonstrated in histological material in the cells of developing
embryos (morulas and blastocysts) as well as in the mucous and sub-

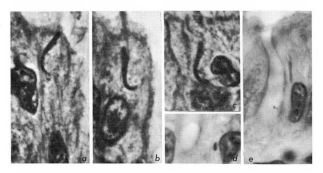

Fig. 7.6.   Sections of cells in the mucous membrane of the Fallopian tube in the rat. Appearances
strongly suggest that the sperm heads have been engulfed by the cells. (a–c) By phase-contrast
microscopy. (d and e) By direct illumination.

mucous tissues of the mother. Subsequently, most of these observations
were shown to be attributable to artifact, such as the scattering of
spermatozoa from areas of high concentration, like the uterine lumen,
to the surface of sections of various tissues by the microtome knife
or by movements of the mounting medium. The remaining observations, which seem quite valid, related to the presence of sperm heads
within cells of the Fallopian tube mucosa (which may have phagocytic capability) or within phagocytes (polymorphonuclear leukocytes)
that had apparently migrated into the uterine tissues after engulfing
spermatozoa lying in the lumen (Figs. 7.6 and 7.7). There was nothing
to suggest that syngamy ever occurred between the sperm-head nuclei
and the nuclei of epithelial cells or phagocytes, but spermatozoa ab-
sorbed under the circumstances described may have antigenic significance.

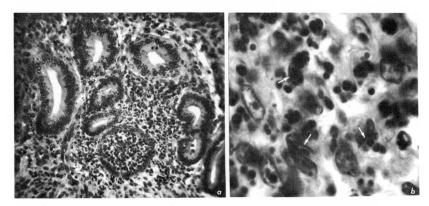

Fig. 7.7. Section of guinea-pig uterus, showing (a) leucocytic invasion of a uterine gland and the surrounding tissue, and (b) a higher magnification of an area in the surrounding tissue. Arrows indicate sperm heads within phagocytes.

Fertilization in vitro

The eggs of many organisms, particularly aquatic species, are fertilized outside the animal body; the gametes in these instances are adapted for function in the external environment. In other animals, many of them aquatic, fertilization is internal, and the spermatozoa are passed from the body of the male to that of the female by various means and often without any exposure to external conditions (see "Mechanical juxtaposition of gametes" in Chapter 4). The gametes thus involved are adapted primarily to function in an internal environment that differs, often radically, from the external environment. Nevertheless, it has been found possible, by experimental intervention, to bring about the fertilization in vitro of eggs of several of the animals in this second group, demonstrating that conditions sufficiently close to those prevailing in vivo have been achieved artificially. These animals include the annelid *Platynereis*, the molluscs *Ensis*, *Teredo*, and *Loligo*, and the tunicate *Botrillus*. Mammals provide a special challenge in this connection, for their internal environment is the most highly specialized, and there is a long history of fruitless attempts and of ill-founded claims of success. Convincing evidence that mammalian eggs can be fertilized in vitro has so far been produced for only the rabbit and the golden hamster. With the rabbit, sperm entry was obtained only if the spermatozoa were recovered from the uteri of mated animals, these spermatozoa presumably having undergone capacitation (see "Egg-membrane lysins" in Chapter 5). Precautions were taken to ensure that the medium in which the gametes were suspended was controlled with respect to hydrogen-ion concentration, carbon dioxide partial pressure, and temperature, but the low rates of fertilization recorded (usually between 10 and 20 per cent) suggest that the requisite environmental conditions are as yet poorly defined. Results reported with golden hamster eggs showed a much higher rate of fertilization (66 per cent), although this was accompanied by an undesirably high incidence of polyspermy (33 per cent). In addition, some 17 per cent of eggs were found to be fertilized after incubation with epididymal spermatozoa, which means that, at least with hamster spermatozoa, conditions permitting capacitation in vitro can be produced experimentally.

Selected Bibliography

The most comprehensive treatment of animal reproduction is to be found in the two volumes of *Marshall's Physiology of Reproduction*, 3rd ed., edited by A. S. Parkes (Boston: Little, Brown & Co.). Volume I appeared in two parts—Part 1 in 1956, Part 2 in 1960. Volume II was published in 1952. The following chapters are especially relevant:

Amoroso, E. C., and F. H. A. Marshall, "External Factors in Sexual Periodicity." Vol. I, Part 2, Chap. 13. Vertebrates.

Austin, C. R., and A. Walton, "Fertilization." I, 2, Chap. 10. Mostly mammals, but some information on invertebrates and other vertebrates.

Bishop, M. W. H., and A. Walton, "Metabolism and Motility of Mammalian Spermatozoa." I, 2, Chap. 9A.

——, "Spermatogenesis and the Structure of Mammalian Spermatozoa." I, 2, Chap. 7.

Boyd, J. D., and W. J. Hamilton, "Cleavage, Early Development and Implantation of the Egg." II, Chap. 21. Vertebrates.

Brambell, F. W. R., "Ovarian Changes." I, 1, Chap. 5. Vertebrates.

Eckstein, P., and S. Zuckerman, "The Oestrous Cycle in the Mammalia." I, 1, Chap. 4.

Hammond, J., "Fertility." II, Chap. 21. Mammals.

Marshall, F. H. A., "The Breeding Season." I, 1, Chap. 1. All animal phyla.

Matthews, L. H., and F. H. A. Marshall, "Cyclical Changes in the Reproductive Organs of the Lower Vertebrates." I, 1, Chap. 3.

Parkes, A. S., "The Biology of Spermatozoa and Artificial Insemination." I, 2, Chap. 9. Mostly mammals, but some information on insects and lower vertebrates.

Walton, A., "Copulation and Natural Insemination." I, 2, Chap. 8. Mammals.

Full and detailed treatment is also provided by the two volumes of *Sex and Internal Secretions*, 3rd ed., edited by William C. Young (Baltimore: Williams and Wilkins Co., 1961). Particularly relevant chapters are:

Albert, A., "The Mammalian Testis." Vol. I, Chap. 5. Including spermatogenesis.
Bishop, D. W., "Biology of Spermatozoa." II, Chap. 13. Mostly mammals, but some data on other animals.
Blandau, R. J., "Biology of Eggs and Implantation." II, Chap. 14. Mammals.
Everett, J. W., "The Mammalian Female Reproductive Cycle and Its Controlling Mechanisms." I, Chap. 8.
Forbes, T. R., "Endocrinology of Reproduction in Cold-blooded Vertebrates." II, Chap. 17.
Gowen, J. W., "Genetic and Cytologic Foundations for Sex." I, Chap. 1. Animals and plants.
van Tienhoven, A., "Endocrinology of Reproduction in Birds." II, Chap. 18.
Young, William C., "The Mammalian Ovary." I, Chap. 7. Including oögenesis.

Treatment of reproductive physiology oriented specifically to domestic animals is to be found in:

Cole, H. H., and P. T. Cupps, eds., *Reproduction in Domestic Animals*. New York: Academic Press, Inc., 1959. 2 vols.
Hafez, E. S. E., ed., *Reproduction in Farm Animals*. Philadelphia: Lea & Febiger, 1962.
Nalbandov, Andrew V., *Reproductive Physiology*. San Francisco: W. H. Freeman & Co., 1958.
Salisbury, Glenn W., and Noland L. Van Demark, *Physiology of Reproduction and Artificial Insemination of Cattle*. San Francisco: W. H. Freeman & Co., 1961.

Several textbooks of a more general character have useful chapters or sections; notably:

Barnes, R. D., *Invertebrate Zoology*. Philadelphia: W. B. Saunders Co., 1963.
Borradaile, L. A., and F. A. Potts, *The Invertebrata* (4th ed.). New York: Cambridge University Press, 1961.
Brimble, L. J. F., S. Williams, and G. Bond, *Intermediate Botany*. New York: The Macmillan Company, 1957.
Darlington, C. D., *Evolution of Genetic Systems* (2nd ed.). New York: Basic Books, Inc., 1958.
Fritsch, Felix E., *The Structure and Reproduction of the Algae*. New York: Cambridge University Press, 1935 and 1945. 2 vols.
———, and E. Salisbury, *Plant Form and Function*. London: Bell & Sons, Ltd., 1961.
Goin, C. J., and O. B. Goin, *Introduction to Herpetology*. San Francisco: W. H. Freeman & Co., 1962.

Gray, Peter, *The Encyclopedia of the Biological Sciences.* New York: Reinhold Publishing Corp, 1961.

Gresson, R. A. R., and H. H. Clark, *Essentials of General Cytology.* Edinburgh: Edinburgh University Press, 1948. Included here because of its three excellent chapters on reproduction in plants, but the book also contains useful treatment of gametogenesis and fertilization in animals.

Grove, Alfred John, and G. E. Newell, *Animal Biology* (5th ed.). London: University Tutorial Press, 1957.

Hall, R. P., *Protozoology.* Englewood Cliffs, N. J.: Prentice-Hall, Inc., 1953.

Harvey, E. B., *The American Arbacia and Other Sea Urchins.* Princeton: Princeton University Press, 1956.

Howarth, W. O., and L. G. G. Warne, *Textbook of Botany.* London: University Tutorial Press, 1962.

Jacob, François, and E. L. Wollman, *Sexuality and the Genetics of Bacteria.* New York: Academic Press, Inc., 1961.

Johannsen, O. A., and F. H. Butt, *Embryology of Insects and Myriapods.* New York: McGraw-Hill Book Company, 1941.

Lagler, K. F., J. E. Bardach, and R. R. Miller, *Ichthyology.* New York: John Wiley & Sons, Inc., 1962.

McLean, R. C., and W. R. Ivimey-Cook, *Textbook of Theoretical Botany.* New York: David McKay Company, Inc., 1951 and 1956. 2 vols.

Mackinnon, D. L., and R. S. J. Hawes, *An Introduction to the Study of Protozoa.* New York: Oxford University Press, 1961.

Mann, K. H., *Leeches (Hirudinea): Their Structure, Physiology, Ecology, and Embryology.* New York: Pergamon Press, 1962.

Parker, T. J., and W. A. Haswell, *A Text-Book of Zoology.* 2 vols. I: New York: The Macmillan Company, 1940 (6th ed.). II: New York: St. Martin's Press, Inc., 1962 (7th ed., rev. by A. J. Marshall).

Pinner, E., *Born Alive.* London: Jonathan Cape, Ltd., 1959. Animals generally.

Stanier, R. Y., M. L. Doudoroff, and E. A. Adelberg, *The Microbial World.* Englewood Cliffs, N. J.: Prentice-Hall, Inc., 1963.

Wardlaw, C. W., *Embryogenesis in Plants.* New York: John Wiley & Sons, Inc., 1955.

Wheeler, W. F., *Intermediate Biology* (6th ed.). London: William Heinemann, Limited, 1962.

White, M. J. D., *Animal Cytology and Evolution* (2nd ed.). New York: Cambridge University Press, 1954. Especially useful as a source of information on chromosomes, meiosis, and amphi- and apomictic development in insects.

Wichterman, R., *The Biology of Paramecium.* New York: McGraw-Hill Book Company, 1953.

Wigglesworth, V. B., *The Principles of Insect Physiology.* New York: E. P. Dutton & Co., Inc., 1950.

Specialist monographs and reviews devoted to the subject of reproduction, or more specifically to those of gamete physiology or fertilization, are the following:

Asdell, S. A., *Patterns of Mammalian Reproduction.* Ithaca: Comstock Pub. Associates, 1946.

Austin, C. R., "Anomalies of Fertilization Leading to Triploidy," *J. Cellular Comp. Physiol., 56,* Suppl. 1 (1960), 1. Mammals.

————, "Fertilization of Mammalian Eggs *in vitro," Intern. Rev. Cytol., 12* (1961), 337.

————, *The Mammalian Egg.* Oxford: Blackwell Scientific Publications, 1961.

Beatty, R. A., *Parthenogenesis and Polyploidy in Mammalian Development.* New York: Cambridge University Press, 1957.

Bishop, D. W., "Reactivation of Extracted Sperm Cell Models in Relation to the Mechanism of Motility," *Spermatozoan Motility,* p. 251. Washington, D. C.: American Association for the Advancement of Science, 1962.

————, "Sperm Motility," *Physiol. Rev., 42* (1962), 1. Vertebrates and invertebrates.

Braden, A. W. H., "Genetic Influences on the Morphology and Function of the Gametes," *J. Cellular Comp. Physiol., 56,* Suppl. 1 (1960), 17.

Bullough, W. S., *Vertebrate Sexual Cycles.* New York: John Wiley & Sons, Inc., 1951.

Colwin, A. L., and L. H. Colwin, "Morphology of Fertilization: Acrosome Filament Formation and Sperm Entry," in *The Beginnings of Embryonic Development,* A. Tyler, R. C. von Borstel, and C. B. Metz, eds., p. 135. Washington, D. C.: American Association for the Advancement of Science, 1957. Marine intertebrates.

Costello, D. P., M. E. Davidson, A. Eggers, M. H. Fox, and C. Henley, *Methods for Obtaining and Handling Marine Eggs and Embryos.* Woods Hole: Marine Biological Laboratory, 1957.

Dan, J. C., "The Acrosome Reaction," *Intern. Rev. Cytol., 5* (1956), 365. Marine intertebrates.

Fawcett, D. W., "Sperm Tail Structure in Relation to the Mechanism of Movement," in *Spermatozoan Motility,* D. W. Bishop, ed., p. 147. Washington, D. C.: American Association for the Advancement of Science, 1962.

Gustafsson, Å., *Apomixis in Higher Plants. Part I: The Mechanism of Apomixis.* Leipzig: Gleerup, Lund, and Harrassowitz, 1948.

Gonse, P. H., "Respiration and Oxidative Phosphorylation in Relation to Sperm Motility," in *Spermatozoan Motility,* D. W. Bishop, ed., p. 99. Washington, D. C.: American Association for the Advancement of Science, 1962.

Gray, J., "Flagellar Propulsion," in *Spermatozoan Motility,* D. W. Bishop, ed., p. 1. Washington, D. C.: American Association for the Advancement of Science, 1962.

Hawker, L. E., *The Physiology of Reproduction in Fungi.* New York: Cambridge University Press, 1957.

Hayes, W., "Sexuality in Bacteria," in *Sex Differentiation and Development,* C. R. Austin, ed. New York: Cambridge University Press, 1960.

Johansen, D. A., *Plant Embryology.* Waltham, Mass.: Chronica Botanica, 1950.

Lewin, R. A., "Sex in Unicellular Algae," in *Sex in Microorganisms*, D. H. Wenrich, ed. Washington, D. C.: American Association for the Advancement of Science, 1954.

McConnaughey, B. H., "The Life Cycle of the Dicyemid Mesozoa," *Univ. Calif. (Berkeley) Publ. Zool., 55* (1951), 295.

Machlis, L., and E. Rawitscher-Kunkel, "Mechanisms of Gametic Approach in Plants," *Intern. Rev. Cytol., 15* (1963), 97.

Maheshwari, P., *An Introduction to the Embryology of Angiosperms.* New York: McGraw-Hill Book Company, 1950.

Mann, Thadeus T., *The Biochemistry of Semen.* New York: John Wiley & Sons, Inc., 1954.

Metz, C. B., "Mating Substances and the Physiology of Fertilization in Ciliates," in *Sex in Microorganisms*, D. H. Wenrich, ed. Washington, D. C.: American Association for the Advancement of Science, 1954.

———, "Specific Egg and Sperm Substances and Activation of the Egg," in *The Beginnings of Embryonic Development*, A. Tyler, R. C. von Borstel, and C. B. Metz, eds. Washington, D. C.: American Association for the Advancement of Science, 1957. Marine invertebrates.

———, "Use of Inhibiting Agents in Studies on Fertilization Mechanisms," *Intern. Rev. Cytol., 11* (1961), 219. Marine invertebrates.

Mintz, B., "Embryological Phases of Mammalian Gametogenesis," *J. Cellular Comp. Physiol., 56*, Suppl. 1 (1960), 31.

Monroy, A., "An Analysis of the Process of Fertilization and Activation of the Egg," *Intern. Rev. Cytol., 6* (1957), 107. Marine intertebrates and fish.

———, "La Fécondation de l'oeuf étudiée comme processes de stimulation cellulaire," *Bull. Soc. Zool. France, 86* (1961), 425. Marine invertebrates.

———, *Chemistry and Physiology of Fertilization*, New York: Holt, Rinehart & Winston, 1965.

Nelson, L., "Cytochemical Aspects of Spermatozoan Motility," in *Spermatozoan Motility*, D. W. Bishop, ed., p. 171. Washington, D. C.: American Association for the Advancement of Science, 1962.

Olsen, M. W., "Nine Year Summary of Parthenogenesis in Turkeys," *Proc. Soc. Exp. Biol. Med., 105* (1960), 279.

Patrick, R., "Sexual Reproduction in Diatoms," in *Sex in Microorganisms*, D. H. Wenrich, ed. Washington, D. C.: American Association for the Advancement of Science, 1954.

Pikó, L., "La Polyspermie chez les animaux," *Ann. Biol. Anim. Biochim. Biophys., 1* (1961), 323. Vertebrates and invertebrates.

Raper, J. R., "Life Cycles, Sexuality, and Sexual Mechanisms in the Fungi," in *Sex in Microorganisms*, D. H. Wenrich, ed. Washington, D. C.: American Association for the Advancement of Science, 1954.

Rothschild, Lord, *Fertilization.* New York: John Wiley & Sons, Inc., 1956. Mostly invertebrates, but data also on vertebrates and plants.

———, "Fertilization of Fish and Lamprey Eggs," *Biol. Rev. Cambridge Phil. Soc., 33* (1958), 101.

Runnström, J., B. E. Hagström, and P. Perlmann, "Fertilization," in *The Cell*, Vol. I, Jean Brachet and A. E. Mirsky, eds., Chap. 9. New York: Academic Press, Inc., 1959. Marine invertebrates.

Terner, C., "Oxidative and Biosynthetic Reactions in Spermatozoa," in *Spermatozoan Motility*, D. W. Bishop, ed., p. 89. Washington, D. C.: American Association for the Advancement of Science, 1962.

Thibault, C., "L'Oeuf des mammifères: Son développement parthénogénétique," *Ann. Soc. Nat. Zool., Ser. 11, 11* (1949), 136.

———, and L. Dauzier, "Analyse des conditions de la fécondation *in vitro* de l'oeuf de la lapine," *Ann. Biol. Anim. Biochim. Biophys., 1* (1961), 277.

Tibbs, J., "Adenosine Triphosphatase and Acetylcholinesterase in Relation to Sperm Motility," in *Spermatozoan Motility*, D. W. Bishop, ed., p. 233. Washington, D. C.: American Association for the Advancement of Science, 1962.

Tyler, A., "Fertilization and Immunity," *Physiol. Rev., 28* (1948), 180.

———, "The Fertilization Process," in *Sterility*, E. T. Tyler, ed. New York: McGraw-Hill Book Company, 1961. Chiefly invertebrates.

———, "Gametogenesis, Fertilization, and Parthenogenesis," in *Analysis of Development*, B. H. Willier, P. A. Weiss, and V. Hamburger, eds., p. 170. Philadelphia: W. B. Saunders Co., 1955. Mostly invertebrates and nonmammalian vertebrates.

Wenrich, D. H., "Sex in Protozoa: A Comparative Review," *Sex in Microorganisms*. Washington, D. C.: American Association for the Advancement of Science, 1954.

Wiese, L., "Gamone," *Fortschr. Zool., 13* (1961), 119. Chiefly invertebrates.

Wilson, E. B., *The Cell in Development and Heredity* (3rd ed.). New York: The Macmillan Company, 1928. This is the classic work on gametes and fertilization in plants and animals, still invaluable despite its age.

Yamamoto, T., "Physiology of Fertilization in Fish Eggs," *Intern. Rev. Cytol., 12* (1961), 361.

Key papers reporting original work are those listed below:

Mammals

Austin, C. R., "Acrosome Loss from the Rabbit Spermatozoon in Relation to Entry into the Egg," *J. Reprod. Fertility, 6* (1963), 313.

———, "Cortical Granules in Hamster Eggs," *Exp. Cell Res., 10* (1956), 533.

———, "Entry of Spermatozoa into the Fallopian Tube Mucosa," *Nature, 183* (1959), 908.

———, "Fate of Spermatozoa in the Female Genital Tract," *J. Reprod. Fertility, 1* (1960), 151.

———, "The Formation, Growth, and Conjugation of the Pronuclei in the Rat Egg," *J. R. Microscop. Soc., 71* (1951), 295.

———, "Observations on the Penetration of the Sperm into the Mammalian Egg," *Australian J. Sci. Res., Ser. B, 4* (1951), 581.

———, and M. W. H. Bishop, "Role of the Rodent Acrosome and Perforatorium in Fertilization," *Proc. Roy. Soc. (London), Ser. B, 149* (1958), 241.

———, and A. W. H. Braden, "An Investigation of Polyspermy in the Rat and Rabbit," *Australian J. Biol. Sci., 6* (1953), 674.

Blandau, R. J., and D. L. Odor, "Observations on Sperm Penetration into the Ooplasm and Changes in the Cytoplasmic Components of the Fertilizing Spermatozoon in Rat Ova," *Fertility Sterility, 3* (1952), 13.

Braden, A. W. H., "Influence of Time of Mating on the Segregation Ratio of Alleles at the T Locus in the House Mouse," *Nature, 181* (1958), 786.

———, "Properties of the Membranes of Rat and Rabbit Eggs," *Australian J. Sci. Res., Ser. B, 5* (1952), 460.

———, "Variation Between Strains in the Incidence of Various Abnormalities of Egg Maturation and Fertilization in the Mouse," *J. Genet., 55* (1957), 476.

———, "Variation Between Strains of Mice in Phenomena Associated with Sperm Penetration and Fertilization," *J. Genet, 56* (1958), 37.

———, and C. R. Austin, "Fertilization of the Mouse Egg and the Effect of Delayed Coitus and of Hot-Shock Treatment," *Australian J. Biol. Sci., 7* (1954), 552.

———, C. R. Austin, and H. A. David, "The Reaction of the Zona Pellucida to Sperm Penetration," *Australian J. Biol. Sci., 7* (1954), 391.

———, and S. Gluecksohn-Waelsch, "Further Studies of the Effects of the T Locus in the House Mouse on Male Fertility," *J. Exp. Zool., 138* (1958), 431.

Bishop, D. W., and A. Tyler, "Fertilizins of Mammalian Eggs," *J. Exp. Zool., 132* (1956), 575.

Chang, M. C., "Fertilization of Rabbit Ova *in vitro*," *Nature, 184* (1959), 466.

———, "Fertilizing Capacity of Spermatozoa Deposited into the Fallopian Tubes," *Nature, 168* (1951), 697.

Dauzier, L., C. Thibault, and S. Wintenberger, "Le Fécondation *in vitro* de l'oeuf de la lapine," *C. R. Acad. Sci., Paris, 238* (1954), 844.

Edwards, R. G., "The Experimental Induction of Gynogenesis in the Mouse: I–III," *Proc. Roy. Soc. (London), Ser. B, 146* (1957), 469 and 488; and *149* (1958), 117.

Hancock, J. L., "Fertilization in the Pig," *J. Reprod. Fertility, 2* (1961), 307.

———, "Polyspermy in Pig Ova," *Animal Prod., 1* (1959), 103.

Odor, D. L., and R. J. Blandau, "Incidence of Polyspermy in Normal and Delayed Matings in Rats of the Wistar Strain," *Fertility Sterility, 7* (1956), 456.

———, "Observations on Fertilization and the First Segmentation Division in Rat Ova," *Amer. J. Anat., 89* (1951), 29.

Parkes, A. S., H. J. Rogers, and P. C. Spensley, "Biological and Biochemical Aspects of the Prevention of Fertilization by Enzyme Inhibitors," *Studies on Fertility, 6* (1954), 65.

Pikó, L., "Étude de la polyspermie chez le rat," *C. R. Soc. Biol., Paris, 10* (1958), 1356.

———, and O. Bomsel-Helmreich, "Triploid Rat Embryos and Other Chromosomal Deviants after Colchicine Treatment and Polyspermy," *Nature, 186* (1960), 737.

Pitkjanen, I. G., "Fertilization and Early Stages of Embryonic Development in the Sheep," *Izv. Akad. Nauk SSSR, Ser. Biol.*, No. 3 (1958), p. 291. Title translated.

———, "Ovulation, Fertilization and Early Embryonic Development in the Pig," *Izv. Akad. Nauk SSSR, Ser. Biol.*, No. 3 (1955), p. 120. Title translated.

————, and M. F. Ivankov, "Fertilization and Early Stages of Embryonic Development in the Cow," *Izv. Akad. Nauk SSSR, Ser. Biol.*, No. 3 (1956), p. 77. Title translated.

Sirlin, J. L., and R. G. Edwards, "Timing of DNA Synthesis in Ovarian Oocyte Nuclei and Pronuclei of the Mouse," *Exp. Cell Res.*, *18* (1959), 190.

Szollosi, D. G., and H. Ris, "Observations on Sperm Penetration in the Rat," *J. Biophys. Biochem. Cytol.*, *10* (1961), 275.

Thibault, C., "Analyse de la fécondation de l'oeuf de la truie après accouplement on insemination artificielle," *Ann. Zootech., Suppl.*, *8* (1959), 165.

Yanagimachi, R., and M. C. Chang, "Fertilization of Hamster Eggs *in vitro*," *Nature*, *200* (1963), 281.

Nonmammalian vertebrates

Blount, M., "The Early Development of the Pigeon's Egg with Special Reference to Polyspermy and the Original of the Periblast Nuclei," *J. Morphosl.*, *20* (1909), 1.

Detlaff, T. A., "Cortical Changes in Acipenserid Eggs During Fertilization and Artificial Activation," *J. Embryol. Exp. Morphol.*, *10* (1962), 1.

Fankhauser, G., "The Organization of the Amphibian Egg During Fertilization and Cleavage," *Ann. N. Y. Acad. Sci.*, *49* (1948), 684.

Ginsburg, A. S., "The Block to Polyspermy in Sturgeon and Trout with Special Reference to the Role of Cortical Granules (Alveoli)," *J. Embryol. Exp. Morphol.*, *9* (1961), 173.

————, "Fertilization in the Sturgeon. I: The Fusion of the Gametes," *Cytologia*, *1* (1959), 510.

————, "Monospermy in Sturgeons in Normal Fertilization and the Consequences of Penetration into the Egg of Supernumerary Spermatozoa," *Dokl. Akad. Nauk SSSR*, *144* (1957), 445. Translated title.

Harper, E. H., "The Fertilization and Early Development of the Pigeon's Egg," *Am. J. Anat.*, *3* (1904), 349.

Kille, R. A., "Fertilization of the Lamprey Egg," *Exp. Cell. Res.*, *20* (1960), 12.

Nagano, T., "Fine Structure of the Rooster Spermatocyte of the First Meiotic Division at Metaphase," in *The World Through the Electron Microscope: Biology*, N. Higashi, compiler. Japan Electron Optics Laboratory Co., Ltd., 1961.

Patterson, J. T., "Studies on the Early Development of the Hen's Egg," *J. Morphol.*, *21* (1910), 101.

Van Durme, M., "Nouvelles recherches sur la vitellogénése des oeufs d'oiseaux aux stades d'accroissement, de maturation, de fécondation et du début de la segmentation," *Arch. Biol., Paris*, *29* (1914), 71.

Yanagimachi, R., "Some Properties of the Sperm-activating Factor in the Micropyle Area of the Herring Egg," *Anat. Zool. Japan*, *30* (1957), 114.

Zotin, A. I., "The Mechanism of Hardening of the Salmonid Egg Membrane after Fertilization or Spontaneous Activation," *J. Embryol. Exp. Morphol.*, *6* (1958), 546.

Invertebrate metazoa

Afzelius, B. A., "The Acrosomal Reaction of the Sea Urchin Spermatozoon," *Proc. Conf. Electron Micr., Stockholm, 1956*, p. 167.

Alexander, A. J., "Courtship and Mating in a Scorpion," *African Wild Life,* *16* (1962), 313.

Austin, C. R., "Fertilization in *Pectinaria* (= *Cistenides*) *gouldii,*" *Biol. Bull.,* *124* (1963), 115.

Colwin, A. L., and L. H. Colwin, "Changes in the Spermatozoon During Fertilization in *Hydroides hexagonus* (Annelida). II: Incorporation with the Egg," *J. Biophys. Biochem. Cytol.,* *10* (1961), 255.

————, "Fine Structure of the Spermatozoon·of *Hydroides hexagonus* (Annelida) with Special Reference to the Acrosomal Region," *J. Biophys. Biochem. Cytol.,* *10* (1961), 211.

Colwin, L. H., and A. L. Colwin, "Changes in the Spermatozoon During Fertilization in *Hydroides hexagonus* (Annelida). I: Passage of the Acrosomal Region Through the Vitelline Membrane," *J. Biophys. Biochem. Cytol.,* *10* (1961), 231.

Costello, D. P., "The Relations of the Plasma Membrane, Vitelline Membrane, and Jelly in the Egg of *Nereis limbata,*" *J. Gen. Physiol.,* *32* (1949), 351.

Dan, J. C., "Studies on the Acrosome. VI: Fine Structure of the Starfish Acrosome," *Exp. Cell Res.,* *19* (1960), 13.

Endo, Y., "The Role of the Cortical Granules in the Formation of the Fertilization Membrane in Eggs from Japanese Sea Urchins," *Exp. Cell Res., 3* (1952), 406.

Gatenby, J. B., "The Germ-Cells, Fertilization, and Early Development of *Grantia (Sycon) compressa,*" *J. Lin. Soc., Zool., 34* (1920), 26.

Giudice, G., M. L. Vittorelli, and A. Monroy, "Investigations on the Protein Metabolism During the Early Development of the Sea Urchin," *Acta Embryol. Morphol. Exp., 5* (1962), 113.

Hagström, B. E., "The Influence of the Jelly Coat *in situ* and in Solution on Cross Fertilization in Sea Urchins," *Exp. Cell Res., 11* (1956), 306.

Hildreth, P. E., and J. C. Lucchesi, "Fertilization in *Drosophila*. I: Evidence for the Regular Occurrence of Monospermy," *Develop. Biol., 6* (1963), 262.

Makarov., P. V., "Cytological and Cytochemical Studies of the Development of *Parascaris equorum* eggs," *J. Obshie Biol., 19* (1958), 338. Title translated.

————, "Cytological Processes of Fertilization in the equine *Ascaris,*" *Izv. Akad. Nauk SSSR, Ser. Biol.,* No. 1, p. 46. Title translated.

Manton, S. M., "Sperm Passage Through Tissues in Rotifers, Turbellarians, Leeches, and the Bedbug," *Phil. Trans. Roy. Soc. (London), Ser. B, 228* (1938), 421.

Moore, B. P., G. E. Woodroffe, and A. R. Sanderson, "Polymorphism and Parthenogenesis in a Ptinid Beetle," *Nature, 177* (1956), 847.

Narbel-Hofstetter, M., "Thélytoquie et pseudogamie chez *Luffia* (Lépidoptère Psychide)," *Arch. Julius Klaus-Stift. Vererbungsforsch. Sozialanthropol. Rassenhyg., 32* (1957), 469.

Rothschild, Lord, and M. M. Swann, "The Fertilization Reaction in the Sea-Urchin: The Block to Polyspermy," *J. Exp. Biol., 29* (1952), 469.

Simmel, E. B., and D. A. Karnofsky, "Observations on the Uptake of Tritiated Thymidine in the Pronuclei of Fertilized Sand Dollar Embryos," *J. Biophys. Biochem. Cytol., 10* (1961), 59.

Speicher, B. R., "Oogenesis, Fertilization and Early Cleavage in *Habrobracon*," *J. Morphol., 59* (1936), 401.

Tyler, A., A. Monroy, and C. B. Metz, "Fertilization of Fertilized Sea-Urchin Eggs," *Biol. Bull., 110* (1956), 184.

Tyler, A., and J. Schultz, "Inhibition and Reversal of Fertilization in the Eggs of the Echiuroid Worm, *Urechis caupo*," *J. Exp. Zool., 63* (1932), 509.

Wolpert, L. and E. H. Mercer, "An Electron Microscope Study of Fertilization of the Sea Urchin Egg *Psammechinus miliaris*," *Exp. Cell Res., 22* (1961), 45.

Protista

André, J., and E. Vivier, "Quelques aspects ultrastructuraux de l'échange micronucléaire lors de la conjugation chez *Paramecium caudatum*," *J. Ultrastructure Res., 6* (1962), 390.

Brock, T. D., "Mating Reaction in *Hansenula wingei*: Relation of Cell Surface Properties to Agglutination," *J. Bacteriol., 78* (1959), 59.

Schneider, L., "Elektromikroscopische Untersuchungen der Konjugation von *Paramecium*," *Protoplasma, 56* (1963), 109.

Vivier, E., and J. André, "Données structurales et ultrastructurales nouvelles sur la conjugation de *Paramecium caudatum*," *J. Protozool., 8* (1961), 416.

Plant Kingdom

Brokaw, C. J., "Chemotaxis of Bracken Spermatozoids: The Role of Bimalate Ions," *J. Exp. Biol., 35* (1958), 192.

Cook, A. H., and J. A. Elvidge, "Fertilization in the Fucaceae: Investigations on the Nature of the Chemotactic Substance Produced by Eggs of *Fucus serratus* and *F. vesiculosus*," *Proc. Roy. Soc. (London), Ser. B, 138* (1951), 97.

Friedmann, I., "Cell Membrane Fusion and the Fertilization Mechanism in Plants and Animals," *Science, 136* (1962), 711.

————, "Gametes, Fertilization and Zygote Development in *Prasiola stipitata* Suhr. I: Light Microscopy," *Nova Hedwigia, 1* (1959), 333.

Manton, I., and I. Friedmann, "Gametes, Fertilization and Zygote Development in *Prasiola stipitata* Suhr. II: Electron Microscopy," *Nova Hedwigia, 1* (1959), 443.

Wilkie, D., "The Movements of Spermatozoa of Bracken (*Pteridium aquilinum*)," *Exp. Cell Res., 6* (1954), 384.

Index

Date Due